scip

Social Competence Intervention Program

A Drama-Based
Intervention for
Youth on the
Autism Spectrum

Laura A. Guli • Alison D. Wilkinson • Margaret Semrud-Clikeman

Research Press • 2612 North Mattis Avenue • Champaign, Illinois 61822 • (800) 519-2707
www.researchpress.com

Copies of this book may be ordered from Research Press at the address given on the title page.

Composition by Jeff Helgesen
Cover design by Linda Brown, Positive I.D. Graphic Design, Inc.
Printed by McNaughton & Gunn, Inc.

ISBN: 978–0-87822-548-4
Library of Congress Control No. 2008928330

Imagination is more important than knowledge. For knowledge is limited, whereas imagination embraces the whole world.

—Albert Einstein

Contents

Contents

Acknowledgments

Many people have contributed to this project. In particular, the authors would like to thank Dr. Kimberly Glass for her original contributions to the Social Competence Intervention Program, as well as the numerous graduate students who were group leaders during the intervention's clinical trial. We would also like to thank our family members and friends (particularly Brit Baker and John Clikeman), who supported us throughout the process, as well as our families of origin, who instilled in us the desire to help others, a sense of fun, and a love of theater. Thanks also to Dr. Sharon Grady, who was instrumental in the program's development and who provided valuable feedback regarding the process dramas. Last but not least, the authors would like to acknowledge the numerous children and parents who participated in the Social Competence Intervention Program over the years. They have graced our lives and work in this field with their unique gifts and determination.

Introduction

Although much attention has been paid to the cognitive and academic difficulties experienced by children with developmental and learning disabilities, less focus has been placed on their social difficulties. Many children with these disabilities are teased by their peers and remain isolated and confused about how to interact successfully. Often when they try to fit in, they fail but do not know why.

Not all children have social difficulties for the same reasons. For some children, environmental factors, past failures, anxiety, or depression may play a role. For others, serious conduct issues prevent them from succeeding socially. Recent research suggests that an important subset of children may have social competence problems because they have difficulty accurately perceiving and integrating nonverbal cues in social interactions, such as facial expressions, voice intonation, and gestures. Specifically, this group includes children with disorders on the autism spectrum—Asperger's syndrome (AS), high-functioning autism (HFA), and pervasive developmental disorders not otherwise specified (PDD-NOS)—as well as children with related disorders such as nonverbal learning disabilities (NVLD). These children have difficulty perceiving, integrating, and expressing information that is presented nonverbally, such as visual-spatial stimuli or nonverbal aspects of language (Klin, Volkmar, & Sparrow, 2000; Rourke, 1989; Semrud-Clikeman & Hynd, 1990). For example, they may have trouble interpreting a very subtle look of fear or understanding that someone may be trying to hide their distress and therefore displaying a smile while having a sad, trembling voice. Many children with these disorders also have attention-deficit/hyperactivity disorder (AD/HD), which makes social situations even more challenging for them. Children with AD/HD may not inhibit their responses long enough to fully process and accurately interpret perceptual information. As a result, they may respond to general environmental cues and establish an overall mind-set that may or may not be appropriate to the situation (Barkley, 1998). In addition, they may be especially inclined to interpret the actions of others as hostile when others' motives are benign.

Across all diagnostic groups, deficits in perceiving and integrating nonverbal information can result in inappropriate behavior and an inability to build or maintain satisfactory relationships. Not surprisingly, research indicates that children with these types of disabilities frequently experience social rejection, isolation, and negative peer and family interactions (Little, 1993). According to research by Gresham, Lane, MacMillan, Bocian, and Ward (2000), 80 percent of a sample of third-grade children at risk for behavior disorders did not have a single friend in the classroom. In another survey (Little, 2002), a large sample of mothers of children and adolescents with Asperger's syndrome and NVLD reported a peer victimization prevalence rate of 94 percent. Three-quarters of the mothers surveyed reported that their children had been emotionally bullied or hit by peers or siblings in the last year. Ten percent of these children had been involved in gang attacks. A third of the children had not been invited to a single birthday party; many were eating alone at lunch and picked last for teams.

In fact, children with Asperger's syndrome and NVLD have been described as "perfect victims" because of their profound social difficulties (Klin, Volkmar, & Sparrow, 2000). In addition, nonverbal processing ability has been related to children's feelings of depression and level of competence (Nowicki & Carton, 1997). Over time, these kinds of social difficulties have been shown to predispose children with NVLD to depression and suicide risk (Fletcher, 1989; Rourke, Young, & Leenaars, 1989).

Clearly, there is an urgent need for programs that create long-term improvements in these children's social competence. Although many social skills interventions for children exist, few have shown generalization or maintenance of effects in this group (Teeter & Semrud-Clikeman, 1997). This finding may be in part because these children's actual social environment is rarely included in the intervention itself. Also, most social skills interventions are general and do not target specific types of needs (Gresham, 1997). Finally, many interventions assume that children can accurately perceive and integrate nonverbal information, focusing instead on training them in appropriate social responses.

THE SOCIAL COMPETENCE INTERVENTION PROGRAM

Unlike traditional social skills programs, the Social Competence Intervention Program (SCIP) blends current research from neuropsychology and information from the field of creative drama to address perceptual and integrative deficits. It offers an innovative, multisensory approach to meet the needs of children with autism spectrum and related disorders in their attempts to fit into their social world. Combined with therapeutic problem solving and discussion in a group setting, the intervention's activities are a powerful and engaging tool to promote change in the lives of children with social disabilities.

Specifically, SCIP is a 16-session intervention based on creative and process drama activities that have been written and modified for children ages 8 to 14 with autism spectrum and related disorders. The program has been inspired by various sources, including collections of drama activities and drama units for children (Allen, 1977; Cresci, 1989; Grady, 1995; Neelands & Goode, 2000; Spolin, 1986); process drama structures (O'Neill & Lambert, 1994); cooperative games (New Games Foundation, 1981); empathic humor workshops (Martinez, 1989); and other methods for teaching social skills to children with NVLD and Asperger's syndrome (Bashe & Kirby, 2002). Many of the tasks and activities are new, however, created by us or inspired by the children with whom we have worked. Other activities have been adapted to address the needs of SCIP participants. The intervention's overarching goal is to retrain participants in the fundamental skills of social perception so that they are able to achieve a more general level of social competence and break the negative chain of social interactions that these children frequently experience.

Program Organization

SCIP is organized according to three stages, which parallel the steps in social perception: input, integration, and output. The figure on page 4 illustrates how nonverbal modalities contribute to the input, integration, and output processes.

- Sessions 1 through 7 target input and focus on the following topics: establishing group identity, emotional knowledge, focusing attention, interpreting facial expressions and body language, interpreting vocal cues, putting cues together, and determining what to do when nonverbal cues do not match.

- Sessions 8 through 12 are designed to aid in the integration and interpretation process. These sessions include activities that focus on taking others' points of view and interpreting several nonverbal modalities within a familiar social context. To facilitate this process, participants are asked to engage in improvised process dramas with group leaders, during which they take on roles and explore the various outcomes of social interactions. Participants are guided to break down complex social interactions into sequential parts, discuss the emotions present, and act out a variety of possible responses.

- Sessions 13 through 16 address output, focusing on techniques to handle teasing and resolve conflict.

Organization of these activities is also structured on two dimensions. The first dimension is awareness of self and others. The initial focus is on children's own experience of emotion and social interaction followed by the perception of interactions with others. The second dimension is complexity of emotions. Target emotions progress from basic emotions (e.g., anger) to more subtle emotions (e.g., annoyance).

Session Structure

Each session follows a structured format, which begins with a warm-up activity followed by review of a home assignment, discussion about the session topic, activities, and a wrap-up discussion to process the group's experience. At every opportunity, peer feedback is encouraged. When interpersonal conflicts or unexpected events arise, group leaders are encouraged to address participants' needs in the moment. Although this book provides step-by-step instructions for conducting the sessions, the format is flexible enough to address the individual needs of participants.

WHY DRAMA?

As mentioned previously, many traditional social skills interventions have failed to address the needs of this specific target group. Social competence difficulties have a variety of causes, and adopting a one-size-fits-all approach to intervention is likely to be ineffective. Several years ago, our research group brainstormed ways to help children who live with social competence difficulties caused by deficits in social perception. We asked ourselves, How might we improve children's ability to read nonverbal cues? Several members of the group had experience using creative drama in educational settings, and we hypothesized that drama activities would be a useful tool to teach the basics of nonverbal social perception. We chose drama for several reasons. First, drama is grounded in experiential, in-context learning and emphasizes the importance of observing the give and take of interpersonal, nonverbal cues (O'Neill, 1995). The essence of drama is social interaction, which involves contact, communication, and the negotiation of meaning within a group context. Creative drama can provide the opportunity to develop imagination, encourage independent thinking and

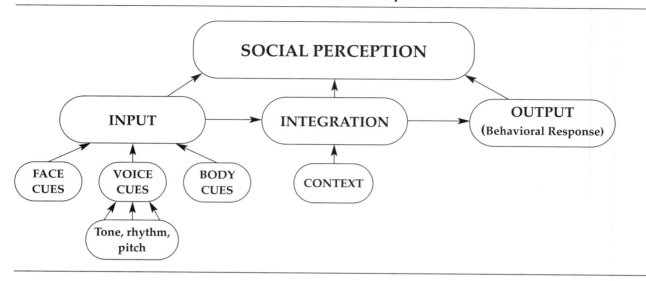

cooperation, build social awareness, take others' perspectives, promote a healthy release of emotion, and improve habits of speech. Drama educators have long proposed that drama activities emphasize imagination, concentration, organization, self-expression, sensory awareness, and positive communication—and that they address concepts of space and distance (McCaslin, 1990; O'Neill & Lambert, 1994; Spolin, 1986). Walsh (1990) has advocated the use of creative drama as a means to foster social skills development, noting that it provides the opportunity to solve disagreements in context. Several scholars in the United Kingdom have specifically emphasized the potential that drama activities have for helping children with autism spectrum disorders (Peter, 2003; Sherratt & Peter, 2002). They assert that allowing children on the autism spectrum to engage in playful and imaginative activity will strengthen the aspects of brain function necessary for more flexible thinking and sensitivity to others. More recently, Attwood (2007) has suggested drama activites as a way to address the social needs of youth with Asperger's syndrome. Finally, drama is fun and intrinsically motivating to many children.

METHODS AND TECHNIQUES

SCIP activities were modified from techniques known in a variety of settings as creative drama, process drama, and drama in education. *Drama in education* is generally referred to as the use of the dramatic process as a way to teach variety of subjects or to supplement a school's curriculum (Heathcote & Bolton, 1995). This methodology, widely used in British education, emphasizes the process of creating drama rather than the production of a performance. The goal of drama facilitators is to provide a safe space for a group to create shared meaning by exploring topics through pretense and imagination.

The use of drama as a teaching tool became widely used when Dorothy Heathcote, a British educator, developed the *mantle of the expert* approach in the 1950s. In this approach to education, an imagined dramatic context is created in which students are empowered by making decisions. For example, children learning about life in a medieval monastery might create the setting of and adopt different roles in a monastery to better learn about the lifestyle (Heathcote & Bolton, 1995). By taking on roles as experts in a shared enterprise, students become experts in the subject matter as well as in the learning process itself. Although Heathcote (1988) developed this method of teaching with the hope that it would be used in general education practice, the method has demonstrated success with a variety of populations.

Creative drama and process drama are techniques used within drama in education. According to McCaslin (1990), the Children's Theatre Association of America defines *creative drama* as an improvisational, nonexhibitional, process-centered form of drama in which participants are guided by a leader to imagine, enact, and reflect upon human experiences. Creative drama involves many types of techniques, including both cooperative and traditional games, story dramatization, and improvisations. Many creative drama games and activities, including work by Viola Spolin (1986) and Nellie McCaslin (1990), have been popularized over time and are widely used in schools, drama programs, and theaters around the world. At the heart of creative drama work is the belief in the process approach; the work is done for the participants rather than for an audience (McCaslin, 1990). In *process drama*, as in the mantle of the expert approach to education, a group and leader embark together on an improvised dramatic journey. Although process drama is similar to the mantle of the expert approach, it differs in subtle ways. In both approaches, participants take various roles in a drama and write their own dramatized story based only on a context, roles, and theme. Unlike the mantle of the expert approach, however, process drama contains an unexpected key conflict or problem introduced by the process drama leader. In process drama, participants may not necessarily become experts on a topic, but they will learn certain skills or lessons as they engage in making meaning out of a narrative together. Participants continually improvise the story as the tensions of the drama unfold, and, in this way, members of the group are led to discover solutions to problems and learn in the process (Bowell & Heap, 2001; O'Neill, 1995; O'Neill & Lambert, 1994; Tarlington & Verriour, 1991). For example, children in SCIP may participate in the process drama "Detective Agency," where they take the roles of detectives and group leaders take the roles of head detectives needing help from the team. Participants are asked to interview suspects and examine nonverbal and contextual cues to help them solve the mystery. In another process drama called "Space Mission," children develop roles as members of a space station to learn about other beings. In the process, they are asked to complete a mission that involves creating a video-recording that will help aliens understand how to read human beings' nonverbal cues.

SUMMARY

The Social Competence Intervention Program (SCIP) is based on a model of social perception that breaks perception down into the steps of input, integration, and output. Drama activities address deficits in social perception because they specifically address the perception of nonverbal cues and the taking of another's perspective and provide the opportunity to solve interpersonal difficulties in context. We believe that this approach is more successful than traditional interventions in helping children with deficits in social perception, especially those with autism spectrum and related disorders. These specific populations are discussed in more detail in chapter 2. The next chapter examines the importance of developing social competence and its relationship to social perception.

Part I

Background and Overview

Chapter 1

Social Competence

What is social competence, and why is it important? The ability to take another's perspective is an important aspect of the development of social competence and emotional adaptability. The ability to be flexible, to change one's response to the environmental context, and to manage one's emotions is crucial for the development of social competence. These abilities allow children to apply learning from previous experiences with others and to interact appropriately in social situations. In order to understand the intervention described in the second part of this book, it is important to understand the theory behind the intervention as well as aspects of the group process that can assist or hinder program implementation. This chapter therefore provides a brief review of social competence theory and models.

Social competence is initially developed from infancy and attachment with the mother. This attachment informs the child's later skills in interacting with others. Trust, social interaction, and understanding of emotions are important skills that begin with the mother-child bond and later translate into relationships with peers. It is rare for a child to be socially competent without appropriate emotional functioning.

Social competence is assumed to be related to social skills, social communication, and interpersonal communication. Social skills are abilities that are repeatable and goal directed (Spitzberg, 2003). Social interaction and interpersonal communication require that a child use social language and nonverbal communication to interact with other people adaptively. The child must perceive the social interaction accurately in order to use and select the most appropriate behaviors for the context. In addition to perceiving the situation accurately, the child must also have the motivation and knowledge to perform requisite skills in a relationship. Without appropriate perception, the child's motivation and ability to do the skill will not result in socially appropriate actions. Similarly, without motivation, the child will not perform the skill.

Dodge (1986) conceptualizes social competence as an interaction between the environment and a set of biologically determined abilities or neurological functioning. Social difficulties frequently experienced by children with autism spectrum and related disorders may result partially from neurological dysfunction. The context of social interaction is also important for understanding the child's social competence. Spitzberg (2003) more fully describes the importance of context in social interactions. For example, social interactions are influenced by the culture in which they occur. Different cultures may have different standards for personal space or voice volume. In addition, social interactions are influenced by the relationships between the individuals involved. For example, children can be expected to behave differently with adults than with peers and to act differently with close friends than with classmates. Interactions may also vary depending on the situation. For instance, a conversation between two children in a classroom may look different from one that occurs on a playground. Children with social competence disorders not only misread social communication, they may also misinterpret the appropriate behavior for the context. When there is a mismatch between behavior and context, the child will often have social difficulties.

Voeller's Diagnostic Clusters

On the basis of research examining children with social difficulties, Voeller (1994) distinguished three groups of children who struggle with social skills, each for different reasons. These three diagnostic clusters include a group with aggressive and hostile behavior, a perceptual deficits subgroup, and a group who has difficulty with self-regulation. Children in the first group tend to act out their aggression and hostility and are often rejected by their peers. They have difficulty forming relationships because they frequently butt into games, do not wait for their turn, and become nasty when they do not get their way. These children are often diagnosed with oppositional-defiant disorder or conduct disorder. The children in this group have been found to have social information processing deficits and often lack appropriate social problem solving strategies. They tend to use the same strategy, either aggressive behavior or language, to meet all their needs. It has been demonstrated that these children will seek out less information from a social situation and that negative interactions are more salient for them than they are for more typically developing children (Crick & Dodge, 1994; Gouze, 1987).

The second diagnostic cluster consists of children who have significant difficulties with perception and, as a result of this problem, frequently misinterpret interpersonal interactions. They may have difficulties understanding social information, reading facial and voice cues, and comprehending nonverbal cues. The most common diagnoses in this cluster are autism spectrum disorders (Asperger's syndrome, high-functioning autism, and nonverbal learning disabilities).

The final diagnostic cluster includes those children who have classic difficulties in executive functioning. Some children in this group may be diagnosed with AD/HD, whereas many may simply be seen as disorganized and flighty. Emerging evidence suggests that the last two diagnostic clusters may overlap. Children with social perceptual difficulties may also show problems with executive functioning and with attention (Carlson & Moses, 2001; Hala, Hug, & Henderson, 2003). When attention and perceptual difficulties co-occur, children appear to experience more significant difficulty in social interaction than when only one of these conditions is present. Not only do such children experience difficulty with perception, but problems with attention often lead them to scan their environment too rapidly to pick up important cues (Semrud-Clikeman, 2007). These children may be able to decipher facial expressions in isolation but when asked to understand dynamic social interactions have significant difficulties (Fine & Semrud-Clikeman, 2007).

MODELS OF SOCIAL COMPETENCE

Three models of social competence informed the development of SCIP. These include the information-processing model, three-tiered model, and theory of mind model.

Information-Processing Model

Crick and Dodge (1994) proposed a six-step social information-processing model for understanding social competence, hypothesizing that difficulty at any step will translate into problems relating to other people. The six steps are as follows:

1. *Encoding relevant stimuli:* Important skills are attention to nonverbal and verbal social cues, both obvious and covert.

2. *Interpreting cues:* Important skills are gained through an understanding of what has happened as well as the cause and intent underlying the interaction.

3. *Establishing goals:* It is important for the child to determine what he or she wants from an interaction and to have an understanding of what to expect from the other person.

4. *Developing a representation of the situation:* In this step, the child must compare past experiences to the current situation. In addition, the child must recall the reaction in the past to his or her actions. This step requires working memory.

5. *Selecting possible responses:* In this step, the child selects from all possible responses based on perceptions of the event and the skills he or she possesses.

6. *Enacting and evaluating the response:* The child acts and then determines how successful the response is.

The figure on page 4 shows the relationship among input, integration, and output (Guli, 2004). As this figure shows, the facial expressions, body language, and voice intonation of others provide the child with information about how successfully he or she has performed skills involved in the six steps of social information processing. If the child's perceptions are inaccurate, these modalities do not provide the feedback the child needs to perform appropriately in the social situation.

Social situations provide a great deal of information at once, and they are generally dynamic. It is not possible to respond to all aspects of the interaction and environment, and most of us select the most important aspects in formulating our responses. Keying in on less important aspects or perceiving them incorrectly often leads to difficulties in relating to others. In addition, the processing of social information relies on a child's memory of previous experiences. Emotional and physiological components of memory are important, and a child who has experienced significant difficulties in relating to others in the past may continue to experience biological and emotional reactions that are inconsistent or otherwise unhelpful. These biological and emotional components in turn influence how a child responds to a current scenario (Huesmann & Eron, 1989). Thus, the child's past social learning experiences come into play in the interpretation of the current event and color the child's resulting reactions (Huesmann & Eron, 1989).

Three-Tiered Model

Cavell, Meehan, and Fiala (2003) suggest a three-tiered model of social competence. The most advanced level, social adjustment, is related to how closely the child's developmental level meets the expectations of teachers, parents, and society. For the majority of children, these levels coincide with chronological age. However, when a child's developmental and chronological age do not match, frequently the child is socially rejected—seen as "odd" and possibly isolated from his or her peers. This isolation further restricts the child's ability to relate to others and to develop appropriate skills. The next level, social performance, reflects how well the child performs in social situations. Important at this level is the child's style of interaction with others. Therefore, parents, teachers, and others must have an understanding of what situations are problematic for the child. The most basic level and the foundation for the other two levels involves social skills, or the specific abilities the child uses within a social situation. At this level, important aspects are how the child responds to a given situation, the child's repertoire of skills, and how the child understands (or encodes) the situation. Cavell et al. incorporate the Crick and Dodge model in the social skills level of their construct.

Theory of Mind Model

The theory of mind model conceptualizes that the social difficulties experienced by children with autism spectrum disorders are a result of impairment in their ability to understand another's perspective, which leads to problems interpreting and predicting their own behavior and the behavior of other people (Baron-Cohen, Tager-Flusberg, & Cohen, 2000; Joseph & Tager-Flusberg, 2004). By age four, most children are able to understand their world and comprehend that others may not see it in the same manner. When there is limited awareness of self and others, difficulties with social interactions are likely and limit the child's ability to share thoughts and feelings with others (Tager-Flusberg, 1999). The inability to understand the differing perspectives of different people has been related to problems with conversational ability (Capps, Kehres, & Sigman, 1998) and poor social functioning in children with autism (Frith, Happe, & Siddons, 1994).

It is highly likely that difficulty with language skills impairs social communication. When a child is taught directly to look at another's motives and feelings, the child is often able to complete this task within a very defined setting. However, the ability to translate this knowledge into a less structured and more dynamic setting does not occur readily and likely relates back to the difficulties in flexibility and social information processing present in many children with social competence disorders (Hadwin, Baron-Cohen, Howlin, & Hill, 1997; Ozonoff & Miller, 1995).

Many aspects of the theory of mind model are also represented in Dodge and Crick's (1990) social information processing model. For example, faulty encoding would appear to be synonymous with the social perceptual skills deficits discussed by Joseph and Tager-Flusberg (2004).

ELEMENTS OF SOCIAL COMPETENCE

Several elements of social competence are important. In particular, these include language ability, understanding of nonverbal cues, executive functioning, problem-solving skills, emotional competencies, and perspective-taking skills.

Language Ability

One of the essential elements of social competence is the ability to converse with others. Such conversations require that the child have the ability to understand another person's point of view and to communicate that knowledge through feeling and words describing emotions (Garfield, Peterson, & Perry, 2001). In this view, conversation and emotional understanding are not separate aspects of social communication but rather are complementary in the sense that they allow children to use language in a meaningful way during a social conversation (Bruner, 1998).

Language is socially learned through interactions with caregivers and teachers. These skills develop as the child interacts with others, and, with the advent of social language, the child is able to communicate thoughts and feelings to others (Saarni, 1999, Vygotsky, 1978). Joseph and Tager-Flusberg (2004) found that when language difficulties were controlled, problems in social perception (interpreting facial expressions, gestures, and voice prosody) were related to difficulties in social reciprocity.

Understanding of Nonverbal Cues

Fast processing of social perceptions is necessary for appropriate social exchanges, and these impressions allow the child to understand the intention of the speaker and to interpret accompanying nonverbal cues. If the child has difficulty interpreting nonverbal cues, it is likely that the social communication will be off the mark and the resulting exchange will be unsatisfactory to both participants. For children with social competence difficulties, this mismatch may result in further social isolation from peers. When language abilities are within expectations for the child's developmental age, the child more easily interprets social communication. However, for many children with social competence disabilities, interpretation of nonverbal cues is faulty, particularly when these cues do not match the verbal exchange. Children with social competence problems frequently experience difficulties with humor, puns, and plays on words because they interpret the language literally, without thinking about the motive of the speaker or the context in which the language is used. As stated earlier, these children must pay attention to the match between language and nonverbal cues and be able to understand the emotions behind the communication. The nonverbal cues particularly important for such interpretation are facial expression, voice intonation, gestures, and emotional context of the communication (Halberstadt, Denham, & Dunsmore, 2001).

Thus, an important foundation for social communication is the ability to recognize facial expressions and match them correctly to appropriate emotions. For most children, this ability develops gradually. Over time, the child becomes able to understand another person's feelings and reactions to what the child has said or done and to adapt his or her behavior accordingly (Singh, Ellis, Winton, Singh, Leung, & Oswald, 1998). If the child has difficulty encoding this information, problems reacting appropriately to stimuli and to peers are likely, generally beginning at a very early age. As the child matures, difficulties increase and opportunities for interaction become fewer because peers do not interact as readily with the child.

Executive Functioning

In addition to language ability and the ability to understand nonverbal cues, executive functioning is an area that interacts with the development of social competence. Executive function consists of abilities that allow the child to evaluate his or her behavior, assess its appropriateness, and make changes if required (Damasio, 1994).

They include working memory (the ability to hold information in mind while solving a problem) and cognitive flexibility. Working memory allows the child to retrieve earlier memories of activities and to apply those memories to the present situation. Cognitive flexibility is crucial in applying learned strategies. These skills set the stage for problem solving, in which the child must select behaviors appropriate to the situation. However, if the child does not encode the interaction correctly, these skills will not be used appropriately. Moreover, if the child does encode the interaction correctly but misinterprets the speaker's intent or emotion, the behavior the child selects is likely to be problematic.

Problem-Solving Skills

Problem orientation and problem solving are two components underlying executive functioning that are involved in social interactions (Shewchuck, Johnson, & Elliott, 2000). Problem-solving skills are the strategies used to understand a problem situation and arrive at the most adaptive solution (Ciarrochi, Scott, Deane, & Heaven, 2003). To arrive at the most adaptive solution, the child must select the appropriate skill and be prepared to change it depending on the situation at hand (i.e., exercise cognitive flexibility). Problem orientation involves the child's past experiences and understanding of these experiences as well as the child's understanding of how social interactions occur. In addition to the child's internalization of past experiences and expectations as to how to handle social challenges, problem orientation involves the ability to take another's perspective (Chang & D'Zurilla, 1996). If the child has been successful in solving problems and understanding others, it is likely that he or she will have higher feelings of self-esteem and of social efficacy.

Emotional Competencies

A child develops self-efficacy in social competence by establishing an understanding of social interactions and developing an internal schema derived from how successful he or she has been in the past in negotiating social relationships (Saarni, 1999). Saarni suggests that the following eight skills for emotional competence also appear necessary for adequate social competence:

1. Awareness of one's emotional state and motivations
2. Ability to understand a person's emotion from nonverbal cues
3. Ability to use emotional language
4. Empathy
5. Understanding that external and internal expressions may not be concurrent
6. Ability to cope with distressing emotions
7. Understanding that relationships are intimately related to how one negotiates emotional communication
8. Emotional self-efficacy

According to Saarni, it is not possible to separate emotional competence from social competence. It is very important for a person to develop both emotional self-efficacy and social efficacy—the ability to deal with situations that arise and to change one's behavior depending on the environment. Social efficacy also assumes that one is open to learning new ways of interacting when the old ones don't work and that one is able and motivated to do so.

Perspective-Taking Skills

As discussed earlier, the ability to take another's perspective is essential for social competence. Initially, children view their needs as paramount to everyone else's and believe that everyone interprets situations the same way they do. As they mature, they are able to understand that others can view the same situation in a different manner. This ability to step outside of oneself is very important for the development of mature social relationships.

The role of executive functioning is integral to perspective taking. It is crucial to be able to take in many stimuli at once and to hold them in working memory while processing a social scene. This ability generally begins to develop at around age 10 and continues to develop through early adulthood. Perspective taking and executive functions work synergistically, allowing the child not only to understand another's perspective but also to process large amounts of contextual stimuli accurately and adaptively. Without this underlying foundation, it is very difficult for children to understand how their actions affect others and to change their behavior accordingly.

SUMMARY

Several models of social competence inform our intervention attempts. These models stress the need to be able to accurately encode social information, to decode nonverbal information, and to use verbal skills to express and share one's feelings and needs. In addition, children's ability to quickly process the dynamic interactions in social exchanges, to recall how these interactions relate to their needs and requirements, and to be flexible in their response to such stimuli are important aspects for the development of social competence. Children who have difficulties with encoding, representation, processing speed, working memory, and perspective taking often experience social problems. An intervention that targets such issues and strengthens feelings of self-esteem and social efficacy is important in assisting children with social difficulties. The types of children who are likely to benefit from this intervention are discussed in the next chapter.

Chapter 2

Target Populations

To help children with social competence disorders develop their social skills most effectively, it is important to understand the nature of these disorders. The social competence difficulties demonstrated by children with autism spectrum diagnoses and related difficulties are similar, and these populations share many other similarities as well. Even so, important distinctions between these diagnoses exist, and these distinctions affect the way children with these disorders behave in groups. In this chapter, we provide an overview of the populations targeted by SCIP and provide examples of how some of the children we have worked with have behaved in SCIP groups.

HIGH-FUNCTIONING AUTISM

Autism is a neurodevelopmental disorder affecting the ability to communicate, form relationships with others, and respond appropriately to the environment. Previous studies' estimates indicated that autism occurred in approximately 1 in 2,000 persons, with males being affected more than females (Tanguay, 2000). However, in recent years, estimates of incidence have been increasing at a dramatic rate, to as much as 1 in 150 for all disorders on the autism spectrum ("What Is Autism," 2008).

As presently conceptualized, autism includes a range of functioning across a broad spectrum. Some affected individuals have intact speech and intelligence, whereas others can be mute, language delayed, or have severe cognitive deficits. Autism is usually considered high-functioning autism (HFA) when average to above average intelligence and intact verbal ability are present. Although some research indicates that the incidence of HFA is rising while the incidence of autism with mental retardation is declining, a number of clinicians argue that this apparent change is due to improved diagnostic methods and a greater awareness of autistic symptoms in individuals with no intellectual impairment (Eagle, 2004).

General Characteristics and Description

The fourth edition of the *Diagnostic and Statistical Manual of Mental Disorders* (DSM-IV-TR; American Psychiatric Association, 2000) has the most widely used definition of *autism*, stating that a diagnosis can be made if a child meets six or more criteria under categories of impairment in social interactions, impairment in communication, or repetitive and stereotyped behaviors. Specifically, a child must meet two criteria under social interactions and one under both communication and stereotypic behaviors. Symptoms must be present before the age of three and usually begin in infancy. The disorder is identified by a lack of eye contact and response to interaction. Difficulties with hyperactivity, attention, and impulses are also common (Tsai, 1999), as are a relative lack of creativity and imaginative play (Craig & Baron-Cohen, 1999).

An additional symptom found in children with autism, though not listed as a diagnostic criterion, is difficulty integrating sensory information. Children with autism often are very sensitive to sensory stimulation (Baron-Cohen, Leslie, & Frith, 1985). Lopez and Leekam (2003) have suggested that children with autism do not find it difficult to put things together; rather, they have trouble making several connections at once and interpreting information within a broad context. Individuals with autism also tend to process information from memory differently than do individuals without impairment (Toichi & Kamio, 2003).

Compared with intellectually impaired children with autism, children with HFA generally show more improvement between childhood and adolescence. Longitudinal data have shown that for children with HFA, improvement in social skills generally leads to improvement in adaptive skills (McGovern & Sigman, 2005). Any intervention that can improve the social competence of children with HFA, therefore, will help them to lead more productive and independent lives.

High-Functioning Autism and Social Competence

Difficulties with social skills are defining features of autism in general, and children with HFA are no exception. In fact, the social skills deficits for high-functioning children may be more devastating because these children are more capable intellectually of understanding peer rejection. Children with HFA appear to have difficulty with all aspects of social competence, including perceiving social cues, putting those cues together with the environmental context, and responding appropriately. Children with HFA have been shown to process faces differently than do typically developing children. These children tend to look at faces in the same way that they look at inanimate objects. They can recognize faces just as well as children without autism, but they do not accurately understand the nuances of facial expression (Deruelle, Rondan, Gepner, & Tardif, 2004).

In addition to difficulties perceiving their social environment accurately, children with HFA also show an inability to interact appropriately with others. Although these children have been shown to have the ability to demonstrate cooperative and helpful behaviors similar to those of typically developing children, they show more "active but odd" behaviors (e.g., a willingness to approach others but approaching in a peculiar manner) than both children with no disabilities and children with AD/HD or oppositional-defiant disorder (Downs & Smith, 2004). Children with HFA have been shown to have problems expressing themselves effectively through body language, facial expression, and voice intonation, and they often feel frustrated when trying to communicate. In addition, their tendency to be inflexible and to fixate on details can make it difficult to relate to them. As a result, these children may sometimes prefer to be alone rather than attempt the frustration and rejection of the social milieu. One young girl with HFA who participated in our project was often quite reluctant to take part in activities with the group, although her excellent verbal skills and appropriate socialization allowed her to be polite in her refusal. Despite encouragement from group leaders and the other children, and despite her previous enjoyment of group activities, she usually stated that she preferred to sit in the corner and watch. Children like her are often thought to be oppositional; however, they are not rule-breakers. They are simply more comfortable when alone.

Many children with autism, including HFA, have difficulties using information from social cues to interpret others' feelings and thoughts. This cognitive deficit is often viewed as a lack of theory of mind (Baron-Cohen, Leslie, & Frith, 1985), or the inability to understand another's thoughts, knowledge, or feelings. Consequently, individuals with autism have difficulty taking another's perspective. In one study, for instance, children with autism were unable to identify how another child would respond to a situation even when they were given information adequate to draw this assumption (Happe, 1994).

Similarly, individuals with HFA have been shown to have difficulty with empathy. *Empathy* refers to an individual's ability to understand another's emotional state *and* to have an appropriate emotional reaction. Those with HFA have significantly more difficulty on tasks measuring empathy than do those without this disability (Baron-Cohen & Wheelwright, 2004). Because of their difficulty in connecting emotionally to others, children with autism spectrum diagnoses often have difficulty developing appropriate ways to regulate their emotions. Most children eventually learn to seek comfort and assistance from others and to express their emotions in socially acceptable ways, but children with HFA must rely solely on self-talk or coping strategies to handle their feelings (Laurent & Rubin, 2004).

ASPERGER'S SYNDROME

Asperger's syndrome (AS) has been referred to as "autism's shadow" (Hayden, 1988) due to its similarity to the autistic profile and inclusion on the autism spectrum. AS is a neurodevelopmental disorder defined by social deficits and restricted areas of interest, as is the case in autism. Unlike autism, however, in AS language and cognitive ability are usually intact from an early age (Volkmar & Klin, 2000).

Though defined by Austrian Hans Asperger in 1944, a year after Kanner (1943) published his famous paper on autism, Asperger's syndrome remained virtually unknown until 1981, when the term was used by Wing to describe a new category on the autism spectrum. In 1996, the condition was included in the fourth edition of the American Psychiatric Association's *Diagnostic and Statistical Manual of Mental Disorders*. In the past, prevalence rates had been estimated as being from 3 to 7 per 1,000 (Ehlers & Gillberg, 1993). The rate has increased dramatically since then, with some recent estimates placing the incidence at as much as 1 in fewer than 300 children (Kadesjo, Gillberg, & Hagberg, 1999). While the reasons for this increase are widely debated and will not be addressed here, the increase itself reflects the increasingly urgent need for effective interventions to target social competence in these children.

General Characteristics and Description

The DSM-IV-TR states that two primary clusters of traits must be present for a diagnosis of AS: a qualitative impairment in social interaction and unusually restricted areas of interest or stereotyped behaviors and activities. The restricted areas of interest of children with AS can result in long, pedantic speeches about special topics (such as railroad schedules or dinosaurs), with little awareness of the listener's lack of interest. Over the years, children with AS have been referred to as "little professors without social skills" (Safran, 2001, p. 154). There is usually no significant delay in language development, although this point is currently debated in the literature. Despite generally intact language abilities, children with AS have difficulty understanding abstract verbal relationships such as metaphors or idioms. These difficulties persist through late adolescence (Nikolaenko, 2004).

AS is generally characterized by major difficulties deciphering nonverbal cues and behavior, such as tone of voice, gestures, facial expressions, jokes, nuances, and body language. Children and adolescents with AS have trouble learning easily from new experience, become anxious with changes in routine, and tend to be inflexible. For example, a child with AS may become upset if an exception is made to a classroom rule. Although not in the diagnostic criteria, other characteristics often noted are egocentric and idiosyncratic behavior; motor clumsiness; inappropriate expression; odd, pedantic speech; impaired use of social language; and unusual eye contact (e.g., gazing off or staring through others when conversing). Other children usually consider them "strange" or "weird" (Attwood, 1998, 2007). Children with AS may have some sensory dysfunction—such as extreme sensitivity to touch, sounds, or smells—and they may engage in inappropriate touching.

AS is usually differentiated from high-functioning autism by the quality of social interaction (i.e., deficits are less severe) and the lack of certain characteristic behaviors of autism. Many children with AS also meet the criteria for intellectual giftedness, leading their parents and teachers to misinterpret their behavior as oppositionality or insolence. Often they are mistakenly placed in classrooms for children with behavior problems or diagnoses such as oppositional defiant or conduct disorder, a situation that sets them up for victimization (Volkmar, Klin, Schultz, Rubin, & Bronen, 2000). Neihart (2000) has proposed that gifted children with AS may not be identified as such because of the similarity between AS behaviors and characteristics of gifted children. For example, both groups often have verbal fluency, excellent memories, and unusual interests.

Asperger's Syndrome and Social Competence

Deficits in social perception—both interpretive and expressive—are at the heart of AS. Children may have trouble at one or more steps in the social perception process, and so difficulties often vary widely among individuals. For example, a child may have particular difficulty understanding voice intonation, expressing emotion through facial expressions, or both. If one deficit is especially marked, this will affect the presentation of the syndrome (Klin et al., 2000; Tantam, 2000). For example, many older children and adolescents do not appear to be deficient in interpreting specific facial expressions at a basic level. Grossman, Klin, Carter, and Volkmar (2000) suggest that older children may have developed compensatory strategies, such as verbal mediation, that younger children have yet to develop. Recent studies investigating these nonverbal deficits in autism spectrum disorders include an investigation of errors in prosody, stress, and resonance (Shriberg, Paul, McSweeny, Klin, Cohen, & Volkmar, 2001) and of verbal bias in the processing of faces in AS (Grossman et al., 2000). Researchers hypothesize that this compensatory strategy may be related to inflexibility in style that is characteristic of the AS profile.

The concept of theory of mind, also widely referred to in the literature on autism, has been defined as the ability to make inferences about others' mental states (Stone, Baron-Cohen, & Knight, 1998). Studies show evidence that children and adults on the autism spectrum show deficits on advanced theory of mind tests, both visual and auditory, though they perform well on simple tasks (Baron-Cohen, Jolliffe, Mortimore, & Robertson, 1997; Happe, 1994; Heavey, Phillips, Baron-Cohen, & Rutter, 2000; Jolliffe & Baron-Cohen, 1999; Roeyers, Buysse, Ponnet, & Pichal, 2001; Rutherford, Baron-Cohen, & Wheelwright, 2002). AS also results in difficulties with empathy, the ability to understand how others are feeling and to have an appropriate feeling in response (Baron-Cohen & Wheelwright, 2004).

Difficulties with theory of mind and the accompanying stereotypical interests of children with AS can exacerbate their awkward attempts at social interaction. They are unable to perceive that others are not interested in what they have to say. One child in our project was very eager and excited to participate in a process drama in which the children took on the role of detectives. He was highly interested in monsters and spent a great deal of time drawing detailed pictures of monsters and talking about different types of monsters. During the drama, he proclaimed himself to be the "monster expert" and spent most of the time interrogating suspects to determine whether or not they were monsters. The other children in the group were much more flexible in their questioning, playing off of each other and the clues they had found. Although he was definitely participating in the activity, the child with AS was completely unaware that the other children were irritated that he was not playing the game in the same way that they were.

NONVERBAL LEARNING DISABILITIES

Children with NVLD often exist in a world that is drastically different from that of children developing more typically. They tend to be withdrawn and socially isolated. Additionally, they may have pervasive academic problems, such as difficulties in arithmetic and handwriting, organization, problem solving, and comprehension of new material (Gross-Tsur, Shalev, Manor, & Amir, 1995; Pennington, 1991; Rourke, 1989). Although it may seem that a disorder of this nature would be deserving of a great deal of attention, the NVLD syndrome is often undiagnosed, and the interventions to address it have not been empirically validated. Clinicians and academicians are aware that these children are different, but they are often frustrated at the lack of programs to assist their work with these children and their parents. The development of interventions in recent years has tended to focus on more prevalent childhood disorders, such as dyslexia and AD/HD. Any intervention targeting NVLD, therefore, is in a position to make an important contribution.

General Characteristics and Description

A nonverbal learning disability involves difficulty processing information that is presented nonverbally, such as visual-spatial stimuli or nonverbal aspects of language. Traditionally, learning disabilities involve deficits in academic achievement, particularly reading; NVLD generally involves deficits in mathematics and in reading comprehension but not in reading acquisition. NVLD has been described as a diagnosis involving a variety of problems, including difficulty with mathematics, social deficits, visual-spatial deficits, troubles with problem solving and organization, and difficulty processing new information, as well as relative strengths in rote verbal skills such as auditory memory and word decoding (Gross-Tsur et al., 1995; Pennington, 1991; Rourke, 1989; Semrud-Clikeman & Hynd, 1990; Voeller, 1986). Although children with NVLD show strengths in rote verbal ability, they sometimes have difficulty comprehending the "big picture" from verbal material, especially when they must infer information that is not directly stated (Humphries, Cardy, Worling, & Peets, 2004).

NVLD occurs less often than other types of childhood disorders such as AD/HD or dyslexia, and therefore it has garnered less attention than these other types (Pennington, 1991). Prevalence rates for NVLD within the population of those with learning disabilities range widely, with estimates of between 0.1 and 1 percent (Pennington, 1991), 1 percent (Denckla, 1979), and 5 and 10 percent (Rourke, 1989) of the general population. The gender ratio of NVLD has been estimated by Rourke to be 1 to 1 and by Pennington (1991) to be 1.2 to 1, implicating males and females equally. Although NVLD is rarer than other learning disabilities, it affects more spheres of functioning that impact overall adaptability.

Not all children with learning disabilities in mathematics necessarily have NVLD. Specific learning disabilities in arithmetic exist without the wider spectrum of deficits characteristic of NVLD. Mathematics difficulties can also occur with other learning disabilities, such as dyslexia. However, the mathematics weaknesses in children with NVLD are often of a specific nature (e.g., they do not result from difficulties in memorization of facts or in understanding word problems) and are found to co-occur with at least some of the other deficits previously stated, such as social skills problems and visual-spatial difficulties (Pennington, 1991). Children with NVLD have particular difficulties with those aspects of mathematics that require visualization, such as comparing numbers, using graphs, measuring, and using figures in textbooks (Johnson, 1987). Conversely, some children with NVLD may not show difficulties with mathematics, especially mathematics that involves rote memorization and other tasks that are primarily verbal in nature (Forrest, 2004).

NVLD is considered to be on a continuum of social competence disorders, bearing resemblance to other disorders on this continuum such as Asperger's syndrome and high-functioning autism (Klin, Volkmar, Sparrow, Cicchetti, & Rourke, 1995; Semrud-Clikeman & Hynd, 1990).

Nonverbal Learning Disabilities and Social Competence

Although specific diagnostic criteria for NVLD have not yet been defined, social competence deficits in children with NVLD have been well documented (Johnson, 1987; Pennington, 1991; Rourke, 1989; Semrud-Clikeman & Hynd, 1990; Voeller, 1986). Socially, children with NVLD appear to have strong verbal skills yet will perceive and interpret situations inaccurately (Hartas, 1998; Johnson, 1987; Thompson, 1997; Rothenberg, 1998; Rourke, 1989, 1995). They will likely have problems with the pragmatic and semantic systems of language and tend to be overly literal (Gross-Tsur et al., 1995; Rourke, 1995). Their conversation does not follow the conversation of others, so their speech sometimes has been referred to as "cocktail party" speech. Their speech is also usually lacking in appropriate prosody. One child with NVLD who participated in our project was so flat in his delivery of speech that he often sounded sarcastic when, in fact, he was generally incapable of sarcasm. Children with NVLD also have trouble generalizing appropriate behavior to novel situations or across situations. Due to their difficulty with social perception, they will often respond inappropriately to others in social interactions.

The perception of faces, voices, and gestures is problematic for children with NVLD, as is the ability to put these aspects together into a meaningful whole. Petti, Voelker, Shore, and Hayman-Abello (2003) found that children with NVLD were significantly less accurate in identifying adult facial expressions and gestures than were children with other types of learning disabilities or children with no disabilities. Children with NVLD show weaknesses in making inferences related to emotional content compared to children with verbal learning disabilities and children with no disabilities (Worling, Humphries, & Tannock, 1999). Change in voice delivery or emphasis is often not detected, resulting in problems understanding humor, sarcasm, and subtleties of speech. In addition, children with NVLD may have problems making appropriate eye contact and keeping an appropriate social distance and may show unnatural affect, such as laughing or talking too loudly (Johnson, 1987). This impaired processing of social cues can lead to rejection and isolation (Woods, Weinborn, Ball, Tiller-Nevin, & Pickett, 2000). Therefore, it is not surprising that children with NVLD show significantly more internalized psychopathology than do children with other types of learning disabilities (Pelletier, Ahmad, & Rourke, 2001).

CONVERGENCE AMONG HIGH-FUNCTIONING AUTISM, ASPERGER'S SYNDROME, AND NONVERBAL LEARNING DISABILITIES

There is some disagreement about the validity of Asperger's syndrome as a separate diagnostic entity, including a longstanding debate about whether AS and HFA are distinct (Wing, 1991) and a newer debate about whether Asperger's actually represents a more severe form of NVLD (Volkmar & Klin, 2000). For example, in comparisons of individuals with HFA and AS on several domains, AS participants were found to have significantly higher full-scale and verbal IQ, larger discrepancies between verbal and performance IQ (Lincoln, Courchesne, Allen, Hanson, & Ene, 1998), and significantly better visual-perceptual skills than those with HFA, although there were no significant differences in gross motor and visual-spatial skills or executive function. Individuals with HFA and those with AS have been shown to be similarly impaired in social skills, and as children with HFA grow older and become more proficient in language, the two disabilities are more difficult to distinguish (Howlin, 2003). Some researchers suggest that AS may in fact be a form of HFA (Gilchrist, Green, Cox, Burton, Rutter, & Le Couteur, 2001; Miller & Ozonoff, 2000). Many research studies often include HFA and AS in a single group, compared with individuals without such disabilities.

In other studies, the neuropsychological profile of AS has been found to match that of NVLD but not HFA (Gunter, Ghaziuddin, & Ellis, 2002; Klin et al., 1995). Also, several studies have found visual-spatial functioning and motor skills to be higher in autistic persons (Schultz, Romanski, & Tsatsanis, 2000). In fact, much of the literature asserts that nonverbal skills are likely to be higher than or on par with verbal skills in classic autism (Sparrow, 1997). Ghaziuddin and Gerstein (1996) also state that a pedantic speaking style can differentiate AS from HFA. This conflicting research calls into question the validity of the diagnostic process and supports the theory that these developmental profiles do not represent distinct entities but instead may be overlapping domains of functioning which, in fact, may vary widely among individuals.

ATTENTION-DEFICIT/HYPERACTIVITY DISORDER: THE ISSUE OF COMORBIDITY

Pennington (1991) defines attention-deficit/hyperactivity disorder (AD/HD) as a psychiatric disorder characterized by problematic behaviors reflecting inattention, impulsivity, and hyperactivity. In addition, children display some difficulties with working memory, perhaps caused by the deficits in inhibition. There are three subtypes of AD/HD: predominantly inattentive (AD/HD-PI), predominantly hyperactive/impulsive (AD/HD-HI), and combined (AD/HD-C; Barkley, 1996; Pennington, 1991). According to the DSM-IV-TR, approximately 3 to 5 percent of school-age children have one of the three subtypes of AD/HD.

AD/HD co-occurs frequently with both learning and developmental disorders. In a study of 15 children with NVLD, Voeller (1994) found that all but one met clinical criteria for AD/HD. Gross-Tsur et al. (1995) identified AD/HD in all of her 20 subjects with developmental right-hemisphere syndrome, which shares a similar profile with NVLD. Attention deficits have also been noted in autism spectrum disorders in several studies, particularly in AS (Schatz, Weimer, & Trauner, 2002). Neurological research suggests a possible etiological connection between AD/HD and right-hemisphere disorders (Brumback & Staton 1982; Hynd et al., 1993).

Some similarities in both the phenotype and neurological profile for NVLD and AD/HD may account for the large comorbidity rate. For example, Rourke (1989) mentions that many younger children with NVLD are misdiagnosed with AD/HD because of early externalizing symptoms that later develop into internalizing symptoms. It may also be that perceptual difficulties make it harder to pay attention. Perhaps the comorbidity rate is due to overlapping diagnostic criteria or a similar etiological basis for the two disorders.

Though some social perception difficulties have been documented in children with AD/HD alone (Frederick & Olmi, 1994; Gresham & Elliot, 1990), the question of social perception problems in children with AD/HD is not entirely clear. Research suggests that children with AD/HD exhibit problems with social judgment based on impulsive responding or inattention to cues, as opposed to actual processing deficits (Carrol, Bain, & Houghton, 1994). In social situations, they tend to scan the environment too quickly to attend to all of the details of their surroundings, especially the more subtle social cues (Semrud-Clikeman & Schafer, 2000). However, Egan, Brown, Goonan, Goonan, and Celano (1998) found that children with externalizing behavior disorders such as AD/HD performed as well as typically developing children on social decoding tasks. A study by Hall, Peterson, Webster, Bolen, and Brown (1999) compared AD/HD, AD/HD with LD, and control groups, and showed that only the comorbid group had social perception problems on a task requiring the reading of voice pitch, stress, and inflection.

Overall, children with AD/HD often exhibit deficits in social competence similar to those seen in children with NVLD, HFA, and AS. Both groups of children have difficulties with the nonverbal aspects of social interactions. For children with NVLD and AS, those difficulties appear to be due to a difficulty perceiving nonverbal cues. For children with AD/HD, those difficulties appear due to a failure to use their skills correctly. In a group setting, both populations may appear to be unable to respond appropriately to nonverbal social cues. However, since the child with a primary diagnosis of AD/HD may fail to notice a cue or respond impulsively, he or she may respond better to activities that stress focus and self-control. In contrast, the child with a primary diagnosis of NVLD, HFA, or AS may respond better to activities that provide strategies to decode and interpret the cues themselves. SCIP program activities will likely help improve both attention and decoding strategies. However, the intervention targets children whose primary difficulty with social competence lies in social perception.

SUMMARY

Children with social competence disorders constitute a diverse and complex group. As a result, they can pose unique challenges to professionals who attempt to help them develop social awareness and use social skills. Although this chapter's brief review provides a general orientation to the common diagnoses seen in this population, if you have not worked with these children before, we recommend obtaining additional support from an expert in autism and other pervasive developmental disorders from within the school district or from the community. Those who have worked with these children in the past will likely agree with us that the rewards of helping these children far outweigh the challenges they bring.

Chapter 3

Empirical Support for the Program

Much empirical support exists for the use of drama as an intervention to address social competence. Walsh-Bowers (1992) cites evidence demonstrating the efficacy of drama activities for enhancing cognitive functioning, imagination, impulse control, social perspective taking, and peer relations (Saltz & Brodie, 1982; Walsh, Kosidoy, & Swanson, 1991). One multimodal drama-based program resulted in improvement in adolescents' interpersonal cognitive problem solving skills (Johnston, Healey & Tracey, 1985). Research by Buege (1993) showed that 32 weekly creative drama sessions were effective in significantly improving the self-concepts of emotionally disturbed students. Yet another study of the use of creative drama techniques in a group of children with learning disabilities indicated significant gains in social skills scores (de la Cruz, Ming-Gon, Lian, & Morreau, 1998).

Additional research documents drama as a specific means to help autistic children (Warger, 1984); facilitate peer interaction (Barsky & Mozenter, 1976); increase self-awareness and insight (Stirtzinger & Robson, 1985); resolve conflicts (McClure, Miller, & Russo, 1992); foster family cohesion (Warner, 1996); improve problem solving (Johnston, Healey, & Tracey, 1985); and improve voice qualities such as pitch, stress, and tone (Stewig, 1972). Finally, Attwood (2007) reports that drama is a useful option to help adolescents with Asperger's. He notes that drama can teach appropriate body language, facial expression, and tone of voice, as well as provide role-play opportunities.

RESULTS OF A CLINICAL TRIAL

A clinical trial of the SCIP program took place in 2002–2003. The study compared a treatment group of 23 children and adolescents to a clinical control group after intervention on various outcome measures, including behavioral checklists, a computerized measure of social perception, and direct observations. Interviews with parents and children and leader journals were also used to gather qualitative information. Participating children had diagnoses of Asperger's syndrome (AS), high-functioning autism (HFA), nonverbal learning disabilities (NVLD), and attention-deficit/hyperactivity disorder (AD/HD). It was hypothesized that the treatment group would improve on measures of social perception and social competence, whereas the clinical control group would not.

Results of the study were extremely encouraging. Quantitative results approached statistical significance for measures of the children's ability to interpret facial expressions and for performance noted in behavioral observations. Qualitative results were even more promising, with 75 percent of parents (12 of 16) and 82 percent of children interviewed (14 of 17) reporting one or more positive changes in social perception or competence after program participation.

A majority of the parents interviewed (68 percent) noticed improvements in their child's interpersonal relations after participation. Parents' comments included the observations that their child joined into more conversations, sought out others more, played better with others, appeared to be handling teasing better, responded more appropriately in conversation, or had made friends. One parent noted the following about her 8-year-old daughter, who had a nonverbal learning disability: "Before the intervention, she would sit in the car with me, but since the intervention she goes, 'I'm not afraid anymore,' and she runs out, and that was a big deal for her, real big. . . . I know she wouldn't be where she is without the intervention. I'm very proud of the changes." The mother of another 8-year-old girl with HFA said that the program "increased her awareness of other kids in a way that I haven't seen before." These findings are quite significant, given the extreme social difficulties experienced by the population. Small yet noticeable changes in children's behavior such as these are encouraging, especially since children can build upon these skills to take future social risks. Knowing that they can be socially successful provides these children with a basis for positive self-concept.

Some of the parents noticed changes in the expression as well as perception of nonverbal cues. The parent of an 8-year-old boy with HFA said that while she observed him playing with a peer, "He was looking at her, making faces to her, making her laugh—he was laughing. I noticed his face shows more expression." Several parents reported that they noticed their children showing more empathy for others, more thoughtfulness, or more awareness of their role in a social interaction. The mother of the 8-year-old girl with HFA mentioned previously also stated, "I have seen her showing more empathy toward [her sister]. . . . If she falls down or hurts herself and is crying, I have noticed that she is showing more attention to her." The parent of an 11-year-old boy with AS noted, "He seems to have improved in being able to perhaps think about what the other person may be feeling."

Some parents noted that their children were using traditional social skills more appropriately, such as apologizing to another without prompting, inhibiting an inappropriate behavior, making better eye contact, and using social greetings. As an 11-year-old boy with pervasive developmental disorder explained, "I just remember if I want to talk to someone I gotta look at them." Social skills such as these are essential to social competence and success with peers. Using the skills they have learned, children are more likely to receive positive responses from peers when interacting with them. We believe that learning these skills *in context*, through the dramatic experience (particularly through process drama), allowed the children to better internalize an understanding of why these skills are so important.

Treatment effects as reported by child participants were also positive. The majority of children interviewed (68 percent) believed that they learned how to perceive nonverbal cues better, especially facial expressions and body language, skills that were directly targeted in sessions. An 11-year-old boy with AS reported after intervention, "I can focus on other people's body language a little bit clearer. I can understand what they're saying with their body language a little bit clearer." An 8-year-old girl with HFA stated that she "learned a lot like about feelings and stuff. I know mostly all those dolls [pointing to dolls on shelf] look sad . . . like their lips are kind of drooping."

Many of the children (43 percent) reported making friends in the group. Several children also explained that being in the group was helping them in school with peers. One 9-year-old boy with AS learned to "ignore people that tease you a lot and stuff and try to find out how feelings are by seeing faces and just hearing them." An 8-year-old girl with NVLD explained, "It helped me to feel more that I had more confidence, so that I could say hi to people without being scared." These changes, as understood through children's subjective experience, are linked directly to specific aspects of the SCIP intervention. Children were impacted by activities targeting the input phase of social competence (e.g., decoding of nonverbal cues, such as facial expressions), as well as the interpretation and output phases (e.g., ignoring teasing and approaching others).

CASE EXAMPLE

Diagnosed previously with NVLD, AS, an auditory processing disorder, and AD/HD by various practitioners, John was a bright, funny, yet somewhat awkward preteenager who struggled with peer relations. John was enrolled in a large public middle school, where he received some services through the special education program. He was referred to the study by the local school psychologist, who was aware of the program and believed that he might benefit from it. Tall for his age and wearing a large pair of glasses, John told us that he was being teased and bullied at school on a regular basis and that his parents did not know the extent of it.

John's mother reported that John felt that nobody liked him and that he didn't really seem to have a best friend. She observed that he was missing out on a lot of social cues, jumping to conclusions in interactions, and failing to make eye contact whenever there was a new situation. She was very concerned about John's isolating himself during the loud lunch hour, partially due to his auditory sensitivity. He would eat lunch with his teacher's aide and, in general, felt more comfortable with adults, talking to them instead of to peers. Stress shut him down. John's mother noted that "a lot of the behavior modification that we do for an ADD child doesn't seem to work." Both parents were open to other intervention approaches.

On John's first day in the program, he found a plastic chair on the side of the room. He sat underneath it, holding on to the metal legs and watching what was happening from there. When we asked John what he was doing, he told us that he was "being a box turtle" and that doing this helped him to feel safer. Although John was 12, he did not seem concerned about how this appeared to the other participants. Leaders soon became familiar with John's box turtle persona appearing unexpectedly. It often appeared in the middle of activities, when John was asked to participate in a way that he did not want to, or when conflict between other participants emerged. John described his behavior as "a stress. It's like when I'm so stressed that I just have to pull away and crawl up in a little ball under a table." When he was not being a box turtle, John was an engaged participant who would share his ideas with a wry sense of humor. It soon became one of the team goals to help the box turtle "come out of his shell" once and for all.

Naturally, things progressed slowly for John. Often, John would be overwhelmed by the noise other children made during activities and would try to leave the room.

In particular, he was annoyed by another group member who had difficulty respecting others' personal space. To prevent the box turtle from emerging, leaders took chairs out into the hall, but then John only recreated the feeling of safety by curling up in the corner of the room or sitting behind the leaders' bags of materials. Although it is difficult to pinpoint when changes occurred, as the weeks progressed, John became more willing to participate and more tolerant of others whose behaviors annoyed him. As he formed a bond with one other child in the group, leaders noticed that the two began misbehaving in a way very typical of their peers, at times disrupting activities by joking or wrestling with each other. Perhaps a small breakthrough occurred when John and his friend had a conflict and successfully worked through it. It is important to note that John did not miss any sessions. Both of his parents were very involved with the program, and they received weekly communications with the leaders about what took place in the session and how John did.

After completing the intervention, John's mother reported noticing some big changes. According to John's mother, his aunt, who hadn't seen him in a month and a half, noticed an improvement when they went on a trip to the bookstore together: "My sister . . . said it was like night and day. She said his face seemed a lot more animated and he seemed to make a big effort to communicate and actually do a give and take in communication. . . . He carried on a conversation with her and asked her questions about herself and prompted her to continue the conversation. . . . She was surprised." John's mother also told us that his grandmother noticed a change during a telephone conversation, saying that he was very animated. Previously unable to carry on a phone conversation, John even asked his grandmother questions about herself and prompted her to continue the conversation, which surprised her. John's mother also noted that John had begun to ask her about how her day was and to show more interest in being with her when at home. Meeting other children with similar difficulties also had an impact on John. According to John's mother, his experience with a child with a severe pervasive developmental disorder, who had much greater difficulty than John communicating, may have helped him gain more insight into his own difficulties.

When John himself was interviewed, he described the program in the following way: "It was pretty much OK. . . . I won't say that it was wonderful and that kind of stuff because it did hold back on my personal life, but it was kind of nice. . . . I got to meet new people—I got to learn how to do this stuff. It would have been nicer if it could have lasted a bit longer, too." When asked if it helped him at all, he said, "I'm a little bit calmer. I can understand people now. I have a social life now." He also reported that he could "understand some of [people's] facial expressions and that kind of stuff" and "communicate better." He admitted that his urge to behave like a box turtle wasn't completely gone by the end of the program but that he did "feel a little resistance" to it. The hardest thing for him was "getting along with everyone . . . especially that one kid." When asked what the easiest thing about group was, he answered, "Nothing was easy," but when asked if he would do it again, he said, "Yes, if I had a chance—yes, I would."

Recently, John's mother was contacted and asked if she would provide some feedback about how he is doing. It has been four years since he completed the study, and John is now a senior in high school. John's mother reports that he has made great progress in overcoming his difficulties. John recently moved to a new city, and though the transition has been difficult, he keeps in touch with friends from Austin and wants to return there for college. John feels free to express his opinions at school, joined an after-school club on his own, and goes to the gym so that he can be more attractive to girls. He no longer receives special education help in school and is completely mainstreamed. Five years after the intervention, John's mother still emphasizes that SCIP really helped a lot and was a key step in helping John realize how his actions affected others.

SUMMARY

In summary, results of the initial clinical trial of SCIP were very promising. Responses from participants and parents shed light on several factors that are key to the intervention's success, including behavior management, organization, communication, good planning, and a thorough understanding of the population involved. One particularly important factor, behavior management, will be discussed in detail in the next chapter.

Chapter 4

Behavior Management

In work with any group of children, particularly those with special needs, behavior management is an important consideration. To benefit from an intervention, students must be cooperative and on-task enough to participate in the activities. And to facilitate the activities confidently, group leaders must have a clear strategy for managing the negative behaviors that are sure to arise.

For children with social competence disorders, behavior management can be especially challenging. For example, because they have difficulty interpreting nonverbal cues, they will not always respond to nonverbal sanctions (e.g., a stern look or a shake of the head) in the same way that other children would. Similarly, they are often unaware of social norms and conventions that help people get along in a group setting (e.g., knowing how to maintain appropriate personal space, providing give and take in conversation). Imagine trying to lead a group activity with the following children, all of whom actually participated in the program: a child with Asperger's syndrome who wishes to talk about George Washington's wooden teeth, a child with AD/HD who will not stay seated, and a child with a pervasive developmental disorder who likes to hug everyone as much as possible. Clearly, a behavior management plan is needed to keep these different types of children focused.

Three different types of behavior management are used within the program. Each type has a different goal and rationale for use that fits within the broader aim of developing social competence. In addition, each type can be easily modified to be compatible with behavior management plans that may already be in place at a given setting (e.g., school) and can be adapted to fit a wide range of ages and symptom severity.

GROUP DISCIPLINE STRATEGIES

Group discipline strategies are the larger framework for maintaining appropriate behavior within SCIP. These strategies help keep the entire group running smoothly with minimal effort from group leaders. They were chosen to integrate smoothly into the context of the intervention, to decrease time spent correcting problem behaviors, and to increase time spent engaged in the activities.

Functional Behavior Modification

The most important component of the plan to change unwanted behavior in the context of SCIP is an understanding of the purpose of the behavior. All children, not just those with social competence disorders, misbehave for a variety of reasons.

Researchers and behavioral psychologists have generally grouped these different types of behaviors into categories. Specifically, children engage in undesirable behaviors in order to elicit attention or power, avoid or escape undesired or difficult activities, obtain a desired activity or reward, or engage in sensory stimulation (Albert, 1996; Brown, Prywansky, & Shulte, 2001). Group leaders must attempt to understand the underlying reasons behind the child's misbehavior in order to respond to it effectively.

ELICITING ATTENTION OR POWER

Many children with social competence disorders are prone to exhibiting misbehavior to elicit attention. Because they are usually social outcasts, often perceived as "weird," these children frequently do not have an ample opportunity to receive positive attention from their peers or adults. Some already may have adopted an identity as the class clown, or they may perceive SCIP's small-group setting to be a safe place to begin to adopt this role to get a laugh from other group members. They may also be trying to get attention from group leaders and other adults in the room by engaging in unwanted behaviors. In a similar way, some children become very preoccupied with getting revenge as a means of eliciting feelings of power or perceived respect from others.

Most adults pay more attention to negative behaviors than to positive ones—for example, a child who is talking loudly to a classmate will get a teacher's attention much more quickly than a child who is quietly doing seatwork. For children who misbehave in order to gain attention, the most powerful intervention involves paying attention to them when they are not misbehaving. It is important to praise them—loudly, publicly, and often—whenever they are on-task, quiet, or participating in the activities appropriately. Of course, this is a great policy to implement for all children, not just those who are prone to misbehave in a bid for attention. By rewarding all group members with praise for good behavior, you minimize the likelihood that any of them will engage in negative attention seeking. In addition, once you model the use of appropriate praise, group members will likely begin to praise one another for doing well, a socially appropriate behavior that should be encouraged.

In addition to praising good behaviors, group leaders need a strategy for handling negative attention-seeking behaviors while they are occurring. Ignoring negative behavior ensures that students will not be rewarded with the attention they desire. Placing yourself in close physical proximity to a misbehaving child while clearly focusing your attention on the rest of the group communicates your disapproval while allowing you to monitor the misbehaving child closely. Alternatively, you may loudly say to the rest of the group something like "Everyone, let's move to this side of the room for now, and when Susan is ready to participate appropriately, she can join us," then lead the group in an exciting game that the group has enjoyed in the past. This will allow you to ignore the misbehaving child and engage the other children in something that will help them to ignore the misbehaving child as well. Another effective way to address attention-seeking behavior is through redirection. Asking a child to help pass out materials for the next activity, for example, provides attention while engaging the child in a positive way.

AVOIDANCE OR ESCAPE

It is quite common for children with social competence issues to engage in unwanted behaviors in order to avoid or escape some activity. Although the activities in SCIP are designed to be fun, and most children report that they enjoy their time in the group, not every activity will be completely rewarding to every child. Many children with social competence disorders also have social anxiety. For these children, any activity that involves interacting with other children will be threatening. In addition, the activities require children to practice skills that are challenging for them. This can cause frustration, particularly when one child is having more difficulty with a particular activity than the others. Children with social competence disorders also frequently have sensory sensitivities, causing them to withdraw from activities when they fear that they might be overwhelmed. Recall John, the child with Asperger's syndrome (AS) described in the previous chapter, who frequently hid under a table with his hands covering his head, loudly stating that he was a box turtle? Other children soon adopted this behavior, and at times we would be conducting activities with only two or three children while the others pretended to be turtles. We quickly developed a strategy to increase their participation: We switched to activities from previous sessions that had been successful and enjoyable in order to encourage participants to reengage.

As with other types of unwanted behavior, the most powerful weapon against escape or avoidance behavior is praise. Children who are prone to engage in avoidance behavior should be praised for any type of participation, however small. However, unlike children who misbehave for attention, children who engage in avoidance behavior may not like praise that is loud and public, particularly if they are socially anxious or prone to overstimulation. Modest displays of praise, such as a quick whisper in the ear, are more likely to be effective. In addition, these children will be more apt to participate if the activity is modified to fit their comfort level. For example, socially anxious children may not be able to speak during group discussions, preferring to sit in the circle and listen. As the intervention progresses, you can encourage these children gently by allowing them first to respond to brief yes-or-no questions. Later, they may feel comfortable giving longer responses.

OBTAINING A DESIRED REWARD OR ACTIVITY

All children occasionally engage in unwanted behavior for the purpose of obtaining a desired reward or activity. The likelihood of this type of behavior's becoming a problem during SCIP is minimized because the activities are designed to be intrinsically rewarding. Good behavior is also reinforced through the reward and response-cost strategies subsequently described. However, this type of misbehavior can still occur, particularly if a child is participating in the group at the parents' insistence. As engaging as the activities are, they are not necessarily as desirable as an afternoon playing video games. Although most children with social competence disorders are excited to learn new skills that will help them to make and keep friends, a small subset within this population have decided that they are simply not interested in social interactions. One girl with high-functioning autism (HFA) who participated in our group made it quite clear from the beginning that she much preferred sitting in the corner and reading a book to interacting with the other children.

Managing undesired behaviors that are performed in an effort to gain a preferred reward or activity is not much different from managing escape or avoidance behaviors. As always, praising and rewarding positive behaviors is the easiest way to promote compliance and cooperation within the group. Children who are clearly not motivated to participate can be praised for engaging in the group in even the smallest way. It is extremely important to avoid forcing children to participate or to engage in a power struggle in any way. SCIP is unlikely to be helpful to any child who feels angry or resentful toward the group leaders. For example, while we were conducting a session in a room that happened to be filled with distracting toys, one child with AS announced that he would not play the game because he wanted to look at the toys instead. We calmly told him that he could do so but that he would not be able to earn his prize for the day. We then engaged the rest of the group in an activity that they had very much enjoyed in the past. The child reengaged in a matter of minutes, and we made a point of thanking him for returning to the group.

SENSORY STIMULATION

The final common reason for misbehavior is to achieve sensory stimulation. Children with social competence disorders, particularly those with HFA and pervasive developmental disorders, often engage in self-stimulation, in the form of rocking or hair twisting, for example. Although these behaviors are not always disruptive to the group as a whole, they are often distracting and usually socially undesirable. For example, one child with HFA who participated in our group was often distracted by his reflection in the mirror and would leave the group circle to stare and put his fingers in his mouth to make faces. Many of the strategies already described (e.g., praise for good behavior, engaging the rest of the group in a more rewarding activity that will attract their attention) are effective in diminishing self-stimulating behaviors. Group leaders are often tempted to ignore these types of behaviors when they are not disruptive to the rest of the group. However, if these behaviors are socially inappropriate, "gross," or otherwise "weird," we are obligated to address them in some way in order to improve a child's social skills. The easiest way to do this is by using social modeling and feedback.

Social Modeling and Feedback

Most children learn socially appropriate behavior through social feedback in the form of nonverbal cues. For example, a child whose playmate backs away learns that he or she has invaded the playmate's personal space. Inappropriate comments and behaviors are often met with a look of disgust. Children learn from others' body language and tone of voice when they are annoying, boring, or otherwise unwelcome. Clearly, children with social competence disorders who are unable to perceive social cues are at a significant disadvantage when it comes to learning how to behave appropriately in a group.

A major goal of SCIP is to help children with social competence deficits learn to interpret these nonverbal cues. Within the group, it is important not to use nonverbal cues to control behavior but to make these implicit cues explicit. Making these cues explicit will likely feel uncomfortable at first and might actually seem rude because we are all used to giving such feedback in a more subtle and nonverbal manner. We do not usually come right out and tell others that we feel annoyed, bored, or disgusted by their behavior. However, without a verbal cue, children with social competence disorders will never get the message.

To communicate that a behavior is socially undesirable requires a sensitive but straightforward approach. For example, a child in our group with a pervasive developmental disability often openly picked his nose. When he did so, we would say to him, "When you pick your nose, I feel distracted and also a little disgusted. If you need to clean your nose, could you please go to the bathroom and get a tissue?" Another child with AS often participated in group discussions with lengthy and rambling responses that were technically on topic but filled with irrelevant details. We would say to him, "Bobby, I am very interested in hearing about how things went at home, but it is hard for me to pay attention to you when your answers are so long, and I want to make sure that everyone has time to talk today. So before you tell us, could you think about what are the most important things and just tell us those?" This strategy can be used in response to more disruptive socially undesirable behaviors. You might say, for example, "Jessica, I am really trying to listen to what Tommy is saying, but I can't concentrate because you are making funny noises."

Social modeling and feedback are also helpful in building relationships among group members. Social interactions are difficult enough when one child has difficulty with social cues, but when several of these children are in a group together, missed cues and awkward behaviors are rampant! Group leaders can intervene in the children's interactions when something important seems to have been missed. For example, when one child with AD/HD interrupted another child's conversation, we interrupted to say, "Wait a minute, Suzy. I think Joey was telling us about how he felt during the last activity, and you interrupted him. Joey, tell Suzy how it felt when she interrupted you." Because Suzy was not paying attention when Joey narrowed his eyes and glared at her when she interrupted him, she needed to hear him say in words that he was angry and irritated.

For some children, social modeling and feedback can actually become the most powerful aspect of SCIP. By receiving immediate feedback on disruptive or otherwise undesirable behaviors, they learn that these types of behavior are inappropriate for any social situation. Many of these behaviors are likely to occur over and over during the course of the intervention. Each time the child engages in the unwanted behavior is another opportunity for teaching. Sometimes, a group leader may wish to model a more appropriate behavior for the child or perhaps remove the child from the group for a few minutes of one-on-one coaching.

Although social modeling and feedback are quite useful in many situations, it is important always to consider the purpose of the misbehavior, as discussed previously. For example, using feedback to address a behavior performed in a bid to get attention will only encourage a child to continue if the feedback results in the child's successfully gaining the entire group's attention. Most other types of behaviors, however, can be addressed effectively using feedback.

The Talking Stick

The idea of using a "talking stick," a small object that group members hold to indicate whose turn it is to speak, is not unique to SCIP. Some American Indian tribes used talking sticks as sacred objects to facilitate group discussions. Many therapists who work with groups or families find this technique helpful. Children who participate in SCIP are often prone to interrupting others and lack awareness of the give and take of conversations. The talking stick provides them with a tangible reminder to take turns when speaking.

We have found the talking stick to be most helpful when it is made exciting or special in some way. A good way to make the talking stick special is to find a strange and mysterious object and tell children that whoever has the best guess about what it actually is or where it came from can take it home to keep when the intervention is over. Possible items include an unusual knick-knack, an odd kitchen gadget, or a small object from a home improvement store (e.g., a hinge, pipe fitting, or drawer handle). Another strategy is to have the children cooperate to decorate a paper towel or wrapping-paper tube. Younger children may want to use glitter or feathers, while older children may want to write their names on it. The talking stick need not actually be a stick. Any somewhat sturdy object that can easily be passed around can be used—even a rock, clay, or a plastic toy.

Reward and Response-Cost Procedures

Rewards are an important part of any behavior management system. They help keep children motivated, increase self-esteem, and provide a tangible reminder of achievement. Although most children are intrinsically motivated to participate in SCIP because they enjoy the activities and want to improve their ability to make and keep friends, rewards are helpful in giving the children an extra boost to inhibit problem behaviors or to encourage participation in activities that seem difficult or scary. The goal of using a reward and response-cost procedure is to increase motivation, compliance, and participation.

In behavioral terms, a *reward* or *reinforcement* is anything that increases the probability that a given behavior will be performed again. We use the term more specifically to refer to something tangible that the child receives for doing something desirable. *Response cost* refers to something that is taken away that will decrease the probability that a given behavior will be performed again. In other words, the child loses something tangible for doing something undesirable.

In the context of SCIP, rewards are typically given when children do something that is important, but not crucial, to their personal success within the group. Response cost ensures that children comply with rules that are essential to the success of the group as a whole. For example, rewards may be given when a child completes a home assignment or demonstrates progress toward reaching an individual goal, discussed next. A child may lose a reward (i.e., incur a response cost) for violating one of the group rules. However, given the tendency of many of these children to misbehave due to impulsivity or a failure to fully understand what is expected in group situations, a system of warnings before taking something away is advisable. The group may wish to decide together how many warnings may be given. Such a discussion and decision would occur during the first session, while establishing the group rules, or group leaders may decide on an appropriate number of warnings. Younger children may need a "three-strikes" approach, whereas older children may need only one warning before losing a reward. We typically allow children to earn three rewards per session: one for attendance, one for completing a home challenge assignment, and one for progress toward an individual goal. Any of these rewards could be revoked if a child repeatedly violates group rules by talking out of turn or refusing to participate in an activity.

The types of rewards will vary greatly depending on the age and maturity of group members, as well as on the group's setting and available funding. Groups of younger children may need smaller and more frequent rewards. When working with younger children, we frequently use a "grab-bag" of small carnival-type prizes (e.g., erasers, yo-yos, stickers, etc.). However, these small prizes are not always motivating enough for older students. For older children, we often use a prize chart, allowing students to earn stickers during each session that will allow them to earn a larger prize (e.g., a T-shirt or a gift card) after accruing a certain number of stickers. It can be challenging to find rewards that are large enough to be attractive and frequent enough to be memorable, but the payoff—participants who are engaged and compliant—is worth it!

Individual Goals

As discussed in previous chapters, social competence problems result from a variety of disabilities. Although children with these different types of disabilities are alike in some ways, they are also quite different. Therefore, in addition to addressing the use of nonverbal cues in social interactions, we also use individual goals to target these children's negative and socially undesirable behaviors.

Ideally, an individual goal for each child addresses a behavior that is both causing a problem within the context of the group and interfering with the child's ability to make and keep friends. Examples of individual goals that we have used in the past include the following:

- *Mind your own business:* For a child with AS who was rigid and inflexible about group rules and therefore engaged in "tattling" on other group members
- *Stay on topic:* For a child with AS who often interrupted group discussions with non sequiturs
- *Participate in activities:* For a child with a pervasive developmental disability who was also shy and withdrawn, particularly during role-taking drama games
- *Stay in the circle:* For a particularly hyperactive child

It is important to frame individual goals in positive terms so children learn what they should be doing, not just what they shouldn't be doing (e.g., "Hands to yourself" instead of "No touching others").

Group leaders define individual goals for each child at some point during the course of the intervention. Goals should be defined far enough into the intervention that group leaders have had time to get to know each child quite well but early enough so each child has time to make some progress. Once goals have been defined for each child, they should be shared not only with the child but also with the child's parents and with the group as a whole. Although each child works only on his or her own individual goal, the children in the group can help one another by offering reminders when someone appears to be on the verge of doing something contrary to a goal and by giving praise for demonstrated progress, particularly when group leaders model these behaviors. In this way, individual goals also help children develop social awareness.

SUMMARY

It can be difficult to manage the myriad of problem behaviors demonstrated by any group of children, and groups of children with social competence disorders can be even more challenging. We have found that a combination of group-based and individualized strategies, such as those discussed here, is most effective in gaining compliance and promoting participants' progress. Managing behaviors within the group is a large part of ensuring that the program runs smoothly. However, seemingly minor considerations, such as where to hold the groups, and for how long, can be just as important in making the intervention successful. These factors are discussed in detail in the next chapter.

Chapter 5

Program Organization and Issues in Group Leadership

Attention to the practical details in running the program are essential in ensuring success, as is leader preparation and training. As previously discussed, children with social competence disorders are often quite sensitive to and easily distracted by things in their environments. Developing the right setting for encouraging the formation of friendships in these children can be tricky. Although leaders may have had many years of experience in working with children, knowledge of the special needs of this particular group and an orientation to the processes of role-taking and creative drama are vital to program success.

PROGRAM ORGANIZATION

The following discussion presents guidelines for organizing the program that we have found helpful—and that you will likely need to adapt to respond to the needs of children in your own group. Although it is important to plan ahead and organize the intervention in a thoughtful way, flexibility, spontaneity, and a sense of humor will undoubtedly be important!

Group Size and Age Ranges

When deciding how many children to include, it is important to strike a balance between having enough participants to make the activities fun and keeping the size of the group manageable. We have typically conducted SCIP with a group of six to eight students and two to three leaders. A low participant-to-leader ratio makes it easier to provide the immediate feedback and coaching that is crucial to improving each child's social expression. Although it is possible to have more children with the help of additional facilitators, too many participants will be overwhelming to the group. Two groups of five would likely be more manageable than one group of ten.

SCIP is intended for children ages 8 to 14. However, it is unlikely that an 8-year-old and a 14-year-old would be successful in the same group. Maturity levels vary widely for children in this age range, and this is especially true for children with social competence disorders. In addition, children in elementary school have very different social needs than children in middle school. In general, we have found that a group including children ages 8 to 11 works well, as does a group composed of children ages 12 to 14. A group of fifth and sixth graders (ages 10 to 12) could also mesh well.

Unless you already know the children before beginning the group and are reasonably sure that they will get along, it is likely that one or two participants will not continue past the first two or three sessions. Because of the extreme variability within this population, one or two members are likely to be significantly higher or lower functioning than the others. Although it is sometimes possible to use this variability to help the group learn flexibility and tolerance, often children who "stick out" will sense that they are different from the others and choose to drop out. Of course, attrition can occur for many other reasons. In any case, it is important to be prepared to lose some children when determining how many children to include initially.

Location

In today's overcrowded, overextended schools and clinics, finding a suitable location for SCIP is no small challenge. However, the importance of an appropriate space cannot be understated. Because many of the activities in SCIP are physical, it is important to have a room big enough to accommodate plenty of movement. In addition, because of the sensory sensitivity and tendency to be distracted characteristic of these children, a relatively plain room is preferable. A gym or a cafeteria would certainly be ideal for SCIP, but a classroom or a conference room from which the furniture has been removed can work as well.

Number of Sessions

As written, SCIP consists of 16 sessions of an hour and a half each. We have found that two sessions per week works best. Meeting twice per week helps the children to build on their skills from one session to the next, while meeting only once per week can lead to their forgetting what they have learned. SCIP sessions may be held once a week if each session incorporates time at the beginning for review of the past session. Supplementary sessions can be added to SCIP to make the program longer, and single sessions can easily be conducted over two days if the children are struggling with particular activities. Although SCIP is designed to build skills from one session to the next, it is possible to eliminate a session or two if time constraints require it. Although we recommend that SCIP be generally conducted as written, the program is flexible enough to adapt to fit a variety of needs.

Parent Communication

For most children, social competence disorders are most crippling in their interactions with same-age peers. However, families are social environments as well, and parent support for the improvement of social competence is very important. As students begin to learn new social skills through SCIP, they will try them out within their families, providing the opportunity for practice and feedback. Offering parents information about the objectives of and activities in SCIP can help them support their child's new skills.

We have found that parents of children with social competence disorders are generally eager to learn about what their children are doing in SCIP. Because interventions that effectively target social competence are few, you may be the first to offer help of this type. Parents are generally grateful for the help and willing to supplement the activities at home.

Each session includes a "Home Challenge" designed to extend the learning experience beyond the group situation. The best way for parents to help their children is to encourage them to complete these challenges, monitor their progress, and give assistance if needed. Some of the challenges require parent participation, but all of them can be completed as a family activity. Encouraging parents to complete the home assignments with their children can help participants get the maximum benefit from the intervention.

Materials

We developed SCIP with the budget-constrained school or agency in mind. Very few materials are needed for the intervention, and those that are required are generally inexpensive. Many of the materials needed for SCIP are probably already available within the setting, and other supplies can be readily purchased from discount or wholesale retailers, office supply stores, an educational catalog, supermarkets, dollar stores, and even garage sales.

Consumable supplies, such as notebooks to create a Home Challenge journal and art supplies, will need to be replaced regularly but are relatively inexpensive. Permanent supplies, such as props and costumes for the process dramas and other role-taking activities, require more of an initial investment but can be used each time the program is conducted. These supplies are relatively easy to obtain, particularly with a little creativity. For example, we created a costume for the alien in the "Space Mission" process drama by using only trash bags and an old belt. In general, the most important requirement for SCIP is facilitators with imagination, enthusiasm, and a willingness to "think outside the box."

LEADER ORIENTATION AND ISSUES

The ideal leader for a SCIP group would possess experience running counseling groups, be familiar with the social competence and other needs of this particular group of children, and have knowledge of the processes involved in role-taking and creative drama. In most school settings, finding an individual who possesses this particular constellation of qualifications is unlikely. Fortunately, so long as these skills are represented within a group of enthusiastic leaders who are willing to collaborate, the intervention can be very successful.

Many group leaders will have had experience working with children in a variety of capacities, including teaching and counseling. Nevertheless, a review of strategies when working with groups, and particularly with children who have social competence disabilities, will prove to be helpful over the course of the intervention.

Although school psychologists and counselors may be familiar with implementing social skills curricula with this population in a more traditional context, it is recommended that they familiarize themselves with the creative drama techniques outlined in the sessions and, if possible, work with creative dramatics personnel in their school district.

Leaders with a background in creative drama may find many of these activities familiar and may even have implemented them with ease with other groups of children. These activities will work differently in this context and with this population, however. Therefore, leaders with a primarily drama-based background will need to become familiar with the target population.

Above all, it is important to stress to leaders that SCIP is both social competence intervention *and* creative drama, a form of group skills training within a creative context, not to be confused with drama therapy or psychodrama. Some knowledge of the characteristics of these children, creative drama techniques, and traditional group counseling techniques will be required of all leaders. Fortunately, it is possible for leaders lacking in any of these areas to acquire sufficient knowledge by reviewing the information presented in this book, benefiting from the expertise of group leaders from different backgrounds, and participating in training sessions before beginning the intervention. With proper preparation, group leaders can become the driving force behind the success of the group.

Preprogram Leader Training

Holding training sessions before the intervention begins is essential to familiarize group leaders with program content and techniques. Although the number and length of such sessions will vary according to the background and expertise of the individuals involved, we recommend a minimum of two leader training sessions, one to review session content and a second for planning behavior management.

The first training session should provide a hands-on review of the session plans in Part II of this book. This type of review includes reading through the sessions, discussing leaders' understanding of the activities, and playing out as many activities as possible in advance to become familiar with them. Doing an actual run-through of activities will help group leaders feel comfortable conducting activities, pinpoint possible problems before they arise, and promote bonding. While the overall purpose of leader training is to share knowledge, the activities should be fun rather than didactic.

A second training session is recommended to address behavior management strategies. It is extremely important that all group leaders be on the same page regarding strategies and remain consistent regarding their use of strategies in order to maintain trust and group cohesion among participants.

Additional training sessions could be added as needed, depending on the needs of the group leaders. These sessions should focus on the topics of social competence disorders and creative drama. If none of the group leaders has training or expertise in an area (e.g., group leaders have experience working with children with social competence disorders but no experience with drama), it may be helpful to consult with experts in the community, such as a drama teacher or a school district autism specialist. Overall, while it is helpful for group leaders to have different backgrounds and benefit from each other's expertise, all leaders will need some exposure to key concepts. This will ensure that all leaders can participate fully and that the goals of the intervention can be achieved.

Postsession Evaluation

Maintaining treatment integrity is becoming increasingly important as the use of evidence-based treatments grows more common. Although this intervention is meant to be adapted according to the specific needs of the children in the group, it is nevertheless important to follow the session procedures as much as possible. One way of doing this is for group leaders to journal after each session, noting especially if the session met its goals. Group leaders may also choose to meet shortly after each session to process how things went. Weekly meetings are also encouraged to plan for the following session and problem-solve about any difficulties that may arise. If a session goes off track, leaders may wish to sit down and decide how to combine sessions by eliminating activities that will still allow session objectives to be met.

Co-leading

While leading groups has its own set of challenges, co-leading groups raises a unique set of issues, including deciding what role to take within group, maintaining open communication among leaders, and processing any conflicts that may arise. We have found that it is extremely important to decide in advance what specific leader responsibilities will be for each session. These responsibilities may include who will gather materials, who will lead discussions and activities, who will resolve conflicts among children, who will communicate with parents, and so forth. Knowing in advance what roles leaders will take is integral to preventing both confusion during session and conflict among leaders. In our experience, how group leaders choose to model cooperation is as influential to participants' learning as is the actual session material.

A Word about Leader Flexibility

Flexibility is always an important component of work with groups of children. Although SCIP activities have been designed to have broad appeal and to build on one another in sequence, it is unlikely that every activity will be wholly successful with every group. If an activity is not working, it may be necessary to modify it (some suggested modifications are included in the sessions), to stop the activity altogether and skip to the next activity, or to try an activity that has been successful in the past. We find that with each group, there are at least one or two activities that the participants enjoy so much that they will ask to do them again. These can be used as reinforcers for times when an activity is not working and participants become frustrated, uncooperative, or disengaged. If leaders find that an entire session is unsuccessful, we recommend finding a way to modify and repeat the activities until the session's objectives have been met. For example, if most of the participants struggle significantly with facial expressions, it is probably best to spend two sessions addressing the topic, even if it means sacrificing one of the sessions at the end of the program. Group members are unlikely to benefit from moving on to advanced activities before they have mastered the more basic skills.

GENERAL GUIDELINES FOR GROUP LEADERSHIP

Following are some general guidelines that are helpful to remember when leading the group.

1. Create a safe emotional space

The importance of creating a safe emotional space cannot be overemphasized. The group should be a place where children feel comfortable expressing their thoughts and feelings without fear of being reprimanded by their leaders or mocked by their peers. Group leaders are essential in establishing this safe environment from the first day, by intervening when disrespect occurs among members and respecting the expression of thoughts and feelings without judgment (even if, in some cases, leaders find them humorous).

A safe space also involves emphasizing and maintaining the confidentiality of group members. Although this is a skills and not a therapy group, as one is traditionally understood, participants may share personal information or expose parts of their personalities that they are not used to showing to others. A general rule to uphold is "What is said in group stays in group." Members are asked not to talk in the group about members who are not present and not to talk about what happens in group outside the group.

2. Take risks

We can't expect participants to take risks with self-expression if leaders do not. Many of the activities may seem silly and may require you to stretch yourselves in ways that you haven't before in front of your peers. If you feel ridiculous speaking in Babble, jump right on in anyway! Modeling risk taking for the group is the most effective way to encourage the children to take risks of their own. If leaders make a mistake, this is a wonderful opportunity to demonstrate that a mistake does not have to mean the end of the world.

3. Praise incremental improvements

An *incremental improvement* is another term for "a very tiny baby step." It may be a change or an improvement so small as to be almost unnoticed; it may even be the absence of a negative behavior or an extra bit of time between negative behaviors. It is important to notice the smallest growth in participants, verbalizing it and praising it so that it is reinforced and encouraged. Many children with social competence deficits are unused to receiving praise since their behaviors tend to elicit frustration in adults and peers. Setting an individual goal addressing these behaviors may be an additional strategy, as has been discussed in the chapter outlining behavior management.

4. Be consistent

Consistency among sessions, among leaders, and among participants is extremely important. If you attend to a child's negative behavior in one session, do not ignore it in the next. If you praise one participant for a certain reason, remember to praise the others for similar behaviors and treat them equally. Most important, group leaders should be consistent in their use of behavior management techniques so participants view leaders as a cohesive team. Words and actions should be consistent as well; for example, do not make promises to participants that you may not be able to deliver.

5. Communicate regularly with parents

Leaders are encouraged to communicate, even if it is only briefly, with parents as they pick up their children to let them know about any progress, difficulties, or conflicts.

Parents can also be advised about specific elements of the session that can be reviewed and emphasized at home. Regular communication with parents is also important to monitor any changes in medication or the home environment. Leaders can help encourage parents to work on the Home Challenges with their children.

6. Be patient

Being patient with the children is very important, especially when a session doesn't go as you expect. When you have planned every detail of a process drama and one participant chooses that day to have his biggest "meltdown," *be patient.* The best lesson that the group may learn that day could come as they observe how leaders switch gears, address problems, and resolve conflict. Seize the opportunity for meaningful discussion if it seems appropriate.

SUMMARY

Program organization and preparation are vital to the success of SCIP, and training for group leaders is integral to a smoothly running intervention. The importance of preparation and comfort with the material and fellow group leaders cannot be underestimated. When working with children, difficulties will always arise, regardless of preparation. We are confident, however, that you will be able to handle them with creativity and grace. As you review the sessions to follow in Part II, remember that every moment is a learning opportunity!

Part II

Session Plans

Before Sessions Begin

Prior to Session 1, group leaders should create the following:

- A parent welcome letter
- A sheet for recording information about the participating child
- A description of the Social Competence Intervention Program
- A map to the location of the sessions
- A handout providing the session schedule
- Brief biographical information about the leaders

Examples of the parent welcome letter, participant information sheet, and program description appear on the following pages. You may reproduce or adapt these items to suit the needs of your own group.

Ideally, parents receive the welcome letter, participant information sheet, and map by mail prior to the first session. The program description, session schedule, and biographical information about the leaders can be included in the mailing, or they can be given out at the first session. In either case, parents return the completed participant information sheet at the first session.

Finally, it is strongly recommended that all group leaders read Part I of this book prior to leading sessions so that they have a full understanding of the overall objectives of the activities.

Parent Welcome Letter

Date _____

Dear Parent(s):

Thank you for registering for the Social Competence Intervention Program! Your child is now signed up for the program beginning on _____. Please bring your child to _____ , where the group will meet. Enclosed with this letter is a brief program description providing some information about what to expect.

The program will run from _____ to _____. So all children benefit from the group experience, we ask that your child not miss more than two sessions. If you like, you may tell your child that he or she will be joining a group of kids your child's age who are getting together to have fun, play group games, participate in discussions, and learn a little more about getting along with others.

Since there is limited space in the intervention, please let us know in advance if your plans to participate in the program change so that another child may be given the spot. Please also instruct your child to leave video games and toys that would distract participants from the activities at home. If your child is on regular medication, please let us know if any changes are made and what we should expect. Parents will not be allowed to observe intervention sessions; however, we are happy to discuss program content at any time.

Thank you again for participating in this program. We look forward to meeting you and your son or daughter in person. If you have any questions, please do not hesitate to call me at _____ .

Sincerely,

Program Coordinator

From *SCIP: Social Competence Intervention Program—A Drama-Based Intervention for Youth on the Autism Spectrum,* © 2008 by L. A. Guli, A. D. Wilkinson, and M. Semrud-Clikeman, Champaign, IL: Research Press (800-519-2707, www.researchpress.com)

About the Social Competence Intervention Program

Thank you for allowing your child to participate in our program! We firmly believe that the support of the entire family is very important to helping children be successful in the program. This handout is designed to give parents an understanding of the program, including background information and a general outline of the activities your child will be doing. If you have any questions about the information in this handout, or about the program in general, please don't hesitate to ask us!

Program Objectives

As you probably already know, the program is designed to help children with social interaction problems. Specifically, it helps children with the nonverbal parts of social interaction, such as understanding facial expressions, body language, and tone of voice. The program also targets some other aspects of interaction, such as putting everything together and understanding the context of social situations. Finally, we try to teach children practical skills, such as dealing with teasing and understanding sarcasm.

Children who have been helped by our program in the past have often been diagnosed with disorders such as Asperger's syndrome (AS), nonverbal learning disability (NVLD), high-functioning autism (HFA), pervasive developmental disorder (PDD), and attention-deficit/hyperactivity disorder (AD/HD). However, the program can help children with other disorders and children without any official diagnoses who have difficulties relating socially with their peers.

The program activities can best be described as a combination of traditional group counseling techniques and techniques from creative drama. The creative drama techniques help us to specifically target nonverbal social skills. Actors use these techniques to learn how to show emotions and interact realistically with other characters, and we use these techniques to help children in much the same way. We combine creative drama activities such as improvisation with group activities such as team building to create a program that we feel is both effective and fun!

Program Sessions

Program sessions are divided into three parts: input, integration, and output. The first part of the program focuses on the input of social cues—in other words, the basic perception of cues). The second part of the program targets the integration of social cues, or how to put cues together. Finally, in the last sessions of the program, we work on output, or how to respond appropriately to others. In general, we start by breaking down social interaction in a step-by-step way, and by the end of the program we have worked our way up to real-time situations.

Part 1: Input

During the first several sessions, we work on trying to establish a group identity. We'll ask the children to come up with a name for the group, and we'll develop some rules that will help the group feel like a safe place. We'll also do some activities that will help the children start to trust and feel comfortable with one another. Next, we'll work on learning how to identify emotions and pay attention to cues. Finally, we'll focus on understanding facial expressions, body language, and tone of voice.

Part 2: Integration

In the second part of the program, we focus on learning how to put communication cues together. Activities help the group understand how some cues match and some do not (when people are lying or being sarcastic, for example). We'll also work on understanding others' points of view. Toward the end of these sessions, we conduct group improvisations where participants will be asked to play a character and solve problems related to social cues.

Part 3: Output

In the final stage of the program, we will participate in activities that will look more and more like real-life social interactions. We will continue with group improvisations and talk about how to deal with teasing and bullying. Finally, we'll review what we've learned and say goodbye.

In the program, the needs of the children are always the most important thing. Therefore, group leaders may choose to spend more time on something if the children are still struggling, or they may choose to skip ahead if the children are doing well. Occasionally, the plan for a session may be abandoned entirely if urgent issues come up. Therefore, it may not be possible to know in advance what we'll be doing on a particular day, but we are happy to keep you updated as the program proceeds.

Home Challenge Activities

At the end of each session, your child will receive a Home Challenge activity that you can use to enrich your child's experience in the program. Some of these activities are designed to involve the whole family together and some are done individually. Either way, the more you can encourage your child to practice the skills he or she is learning in the sessions, the more improvement you can expect to see! These activities offer the opportunity to write, draw, or discuss what your child is learning in the sessions. In addition to the Home Challenge activities, you can encourage your child to journal about anything related to the program or their day-to-day social interactions.

We encourage you to continue to be as involved as possible in the development of your child's social skills. The activities described here are just a starting point, and we hope you will be creative in thinking of other ways to challenge your child. Look for moments in your everyday life to help your child grow and interact better with others. We wish you and your family the best of luck and thank you again for participating!

Participant Information Sheet

Child's name _____ Date of birth _____

Parent's name _____

Address _____

Home phone _____ Cell phone _____

E-mail address _____

What are your child's strengths and weaknesses?

_____

_____

Has your child ever participated in a group intervention or counseling before? If so, please explain.

_____

_____

Is your child on any medication? If so, what?

_____

_____

Does your child have any allergies or other medical conditions that we should be aware of?

_____

_____

Is there anything else that you believe we should know about your child?

_____

_____

From *SCIP: Social Competence Intervention Program—A Drama-Based Intervention for Youth on the Autism Spectrum,* © 2008 by L. A. Guli, A. D. Wilkinson, and M. Semrud-Clikeman, Champaign, IL: Research Press (800-519-2707, www.researchpress.com)

Session 1

Establishing Group Identity

OBJECTIVES

- Make introductions.
- Establish group identity through discussion and cooperative activities.
- Establish the group as a place where it is safe to share feelings, express personalities, and ask questions.
- Create group guidelines.
- Normalize difficult feelings participants might experience when meeting new people.
- Begin expressing thoughts and feelings about the group experience in the form of a Home Challenge assignment.

MATERIALS

Talking stick

Blank name tags and markers

Easel pad or poster board

Copies of the People Hunt handout and Home Challenge assignment

PROCEDURE

Introduction and Welcome

As participants are dropped off, collect the participant information sheets.

1. As participants enter the room, welcome them with enthusiasm and give them a blank name tag and a marker. Direct them to sit in a spot in a circle on the floor where they can work on their tags. Ask them to write their name on the tag and decorate it as they choose. (If the room is carpeted, participants and leaders may take off their shoes and leave them at the door.)

2. Begin the session by joining the circle and having each leader give a brief introduction. Explain what group is about and what kinds of activities the group will do (playing group games, talking about things that help us make friends and get along with others, doing drama activities, and taking fun risks).

3. Encourage participants to talk about what they think the group will be like and why they think they are there. Make an effort to correct any misconceptions about the group or ideas that might reflect low self-esteem.

Warm-Up

NAME GAME

Everyone stands in a circle. Beginning with a group leader, each person says his or her name, making a movement as they do so (e.g., putting hands on head, turning around, throwing arms up in the air, jumping up and down). The whole group then says the person's name and imitates the movement. After the first person, the group repeats all the names and movements from the beginning, adding the most recent one. If a participant doesn't know what movement to make, a leader may offer a suggestion.

People Hunt

1. Give each participant a People Hunt handout. Ask participants to look for others in the group with the characteristics listed on the sheet. Challenge them to speak to each person in the group at least once and fill their sheet up with names. To keep participants mingling, they may ask the same person to answer no more than two questions. If a participant refuses to approach anyone, don't force the issue. Rather, help the participant get the sheet filled out by answering some of the questions yourself, calling another child over, giving suggestions and encouragement, and so forth.

2. After several minutes, or when it appears that most participants have their sheets filled, call the group back to the sitting circle. Participants can share their answers if they wish. Emphasize the commonality among participants, praise their participation, and normalize any shyness that occurs when meeting new people.

Establish a Group Name and Group Guidelines

1. In the sitting circle, encourage group members to brainstorm ideas for group names and then vote to make a decision. Steer the group away from names that imply negative characteristics (e.g., "Freaks") and encourage empowering, positive names (e.g., "Wizards," "Friend Masters," "Dolphins"). Be prepared to help participants resolve any conflicts that arise over this decision.

2. After participants have decided on a group name, explain that the group is a safe place, a place where people can be themselves and not be afraid to express their ideas or feelings. Ask the group to brainstorm some guidelines to ensure that each person in the group feels safe. Write ideas on the easel pad or poster board as they are suggested. For example:

   • Be nice to other participants.
   • Listen when someone else is talking.
   • Respect your peers.
   • Use constructive criticism.

- Try new things.
- Leave violence outside the door.
- Keep group conversations private.
- Do not touch other people unless you have their permission.
- Have fun!

Add additional guidelines if appropriate. Examples of guidelines you could add include staying with a group leader at all times, keeping your hands to yourself unless touching someone else is part of a game, using appropriate language, and so on. Accept all ideas, but reword them for clarity if necessary. It is important that each participant knows what each guideline means and will look like. Display a final set of group guidelines in the room during all sessions if possible.

Talking Stick

1. Show participants the talking stick you have chosen and explain that some American Indian tribes used a talking stick in meetings among chiefs to show who was talking and should be listened to. In group, whoever's turn it is to talk holds the talking stick. This is a sign that other people should give attention to that person.

2. Ask the group why it is important to listen when someone else is talking. Is this hard or easy?

3. Explain that the talking stick will not always be necessary but that it is a useful tool to help discussions go smoothly when everyone wants to talk at the same time.

Knee to Knee

1. Put participants into pairs and explain that the partners will follow the directions one of the leaders calls out. For example, if the leader says, "Hand to foot," then each person must touch their hand to their partner's foot. If the leader says, "Knee to knee," then partners touch knees.

2. Continue to give different instructions. Suggestions: Elbow to elbow, hand to hand, foot to foot, back of head to back of head, shoulder to shoulder, back to back, ear to ear, nose to nose, knee to shoulder, and chin to elbow. Partners must follow directions as fast as they are called. You can call a few difficult or silly combinations (e.g., "Ear to knee") if you wish. Encourage participants to be gentle as they follow the instructions.

Because this activity involves physical contact, participants may refuse to play or become overly aggressive with their partners. Even though these risks exist, the activity provides a rich opportunity for breaking the ice and for leaders to begin to see how individual group members react in situations that require participation. If participants do not want to touch, they may keep a few inches of space between each other during the activity.

Discussion

1. Have the group sit in a circle again and discuss getting to know new people. Sample questions for the group:

   - What is easy or difficult about meeting new people?
   - How do we make friends?
   - How do we let someone know that we want to be friends?
   - How do you like someone to let you know that they want to be friends?
   - How do you feel in new situations?
   - What do you think other people feel like in new situations?

     Leaders may share their own stories about times they felt strange being in a new situation with new people.

2. Praise participants for their good job of meeting others and making friends today.

Wrap-up

1. Discuss session content. Questions to the group could include the following:

   - What was today like for you?
   - Was it what you expected? If not, how was it different?
   - Did anything surprise you?

2. Give each participant a copy of the Home Challenge. Read over the challenge and answer any questions participants may have. Explain that they can write about their feelings, draw a picture, or discuss their thoughts with their parents. Let them know that they will have a chance to share their responses to the challenge at the beginning of the next session.

3. Praise all the group members for being there and acknowledge their participation. Let them know that you are glad they are part of the group and are looking forward to seeing them next time!

4. At the end of the session, conduct the following activity. Doing so takes less than a minute and helps create a bond among group members. In fact, it is a good way to end every session, if time permits.

ELECTRIC CHARGE

Have everyone hold hands. One person begins by gently squeezing the hand of the person next to them, as if passing around a charge of electricity. When each person feels their hand being squeezed on one side, they squeeze the hand of the next person and so pass around the "electricity." See how fast the electricity can be passed around the circle. The group can try this with their eyes closed. Try again so the squeezing continues without stopping at the first person. As the electricity travels around the circle, the speed should increase. After trying it in one direction, the group can switch directions. The group can also cross their own arms and grab the hands of the person next to them (who is also crossing their arms) and try it this way, which is a little more confusing!

> Since many participants may have tactile sensitivity, they may be overwhelmed by this initial physical contact. If a participant is unwilling to hold another participant's hand, don't force the situation. You can encourage the participant to hold onto the shirttail of the next person and tug it instead of squeezing the person's hand. It is more important for participants to engage in the group activity than it is for them to do it "right." Caution participants not to squeeze too hard.

People Hunt

Name _____ Date _____

Find someone who . . .

- likes to read. (What?) _____

- has taken a music lesson. (What instrument?) _____

- has played on a sports team. (Which?) _____

- likes to paint or draw. _____

- has a pet. (What is its name?) _____

- has a scar. (Where and how did they get it?) _____

- can say a sentence in another language. _____

- bites their nails. _____

- likes pizza with mushrooms. _____

- hates math. _____

- has a favorite video game. (What?) _____

Session 1 Home Challenge

How did you feel about your first day in the group? Did you like it? Why or why not?

You can write about your feelings, draw a picture, or discuss your thoughts with your parents.

Session 2

Focusing Attention

OBJECTIVES

- Discuss how paying attention is an important part of getting along with others.
- Practice focusing attention and exercising self-control in both visual and auditory modalities.
- Begin to give and take cues with a partner.
- Increase trust and cohesion among participants.

MATERIALS

Talking stick

Copies of the Home Challenge assignment

PROCEDURE

Warm-up

Repeat the Name Game, described in Session 1, or conduct the following warm-up activity.

ONE LITTLE THING

Have the group form a circle, with one participant standing in the middle. This participant slowly turns around for about a minute so everyone in the circle has a chance to observe the person closely. The participant then leaves the room and changes "one little thing" about the way they look. For example, they might untie one shoe or move their watch from one wrist to the other. When they return, the other participants see if they can spot the change. Guide the participants to raise their hands to make guesses. To make this game more difficult, instruct the person who will leave the room to change two or more small things about the way they look.

Home Challenge Review

Encourage participants to share their responses to the Home Challenge, to describe their feelings about the first session. Normalize the feelings that participants express and emphasize listening to the speaker when it is the speaker's turn to talk, using the talking stick, as appropriate. As participants share, ask others if they had similar reactions.

It is important not to force anyone to share an experience. If no one wants to volunteer, begin a discussion about what it is like to share their experiences (maybe a little scary?).

Discussion

Lead a discussion about why it is important to pay close attention in social situations. Here are some sample questions to get the discussion started:

- Is it important to pay attention when you're in a group?
- Why is paying attention to others so important?
- What can you learn by paying attention to others?
- What kinds of things should you pay attention to when you're in a group?
- What kinds of things can make it easier or harder to pay attention?
- What do you do to help yourself pay attention?

Clones

Have one leader ask for a volunteer to help model this activity for participants first. The activity is done in silence, without touching.

1. Invite participants to choose partners (or pair them up yourself). One partner is the "original," and the other is the "clone." Have partners face each other, then ask them to look each other in the eyes. The original will, very slowly, start to move. The clone should copy the movement as accurately as possible so it appears that they are moving at the same time.

2. Encourage the original to move slowly at first, using very simple movements and then gradually speeding up, always making sure that the clone can keep up. (Someone observing the pair should have a hard time deciding who is the original and who is the clone.)

3. After a while, have participants switch roles. You can encourage them to be creative. Participants can incorporate facial expressions, sit down, or turn to the side, but they should keep eye contact at all times.

To avoid arguments about who goes first, choose initial roles for the partners based on whose name comes first in the alphabet.

Who Started It?

1. Have participants sit in a circle. One person is the "guesser," who goes out of the room. After the guesser has left the room, someone else in the group is chosen as the "leader." The leader begins a repetitive movement that the rest of the circle imitates (e.g., snapping fingers, clapping, touching toes). From time to time, the leader changes the movement. The object of the game is to have the group copy

the leader and switch movements as fast as they can so the guesser can't tell who is initiating the movement.

2. When it looks as though the group is working together, invite the guesser to return to the center of the circle and try to guess who is leading the motion. The group tries to make it harder for the guesser by not looking directly at the person starting the motion. Allow the guesser to make three guesses.

3. If time allows, give every participant an opportunity to be either leader or guesser.

4. Discuss the activity with the group. Questions may include the following:

   - What did you pay attention to?
   - What clues helped you know who the leader was?
   - What strategies helped you narrow down your choices?
   - How was attention an important part of this game?

Super-Powered Hearing

1. Ask participants to spread out in the room, lie on their backs, and close their eyes. Tell them that they are going to find out how powerful their sense of hearing really is. Ask them to be quiet and listen very carefully—to actually send their hearing out into the room and listen to every noise they can.

2. After a minute, ask participants to send their hearing out beyond the room, into the building. What do they hear outside of the room that tells them about what is going on in other parts of the building?

3. After this, ask them to imagine that they can send their hearing out into the world. Ask participants whether they can hear any sounds from the street. If windows are open, can they hear any sounds from nature or any machines from far away?

4. Have participants sit up and discuss their experience: What did they hear? What did they focus their attention on? Did they hear others breathing? Did they hear voices of other people in the building? Did they hear the hum of the air conditioner or a car passing by? Are they surprised at how powerful their hearing is when they really focus it? Some participants may claim to have heard impossible things (e.g., someone shouting far across town or in another state). Accept all answers, even creative products of the imagination!

Wrap-up

1. Discuss session content. Questions to the group could include the following:

   - Why is it important to pay attention?
   - Did you learn any new ways to help yourself pay attention?
   - When were some times today that you were focusing your attention?
   - What were some things today that made it difficult for you to pay attention?

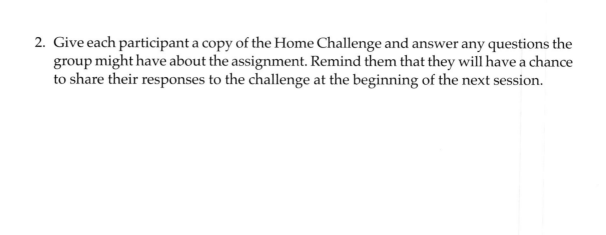

2. Give each participant a copy of the Home Challenge and answer any questions the group might have about the assignment. Remind them that they will have a chance to share their responses to the challenge at the beginning of the next session.

Session 2 Home Challenge

Find a spot at home, preferably outside, where you can quietly sit down. Take some time to look at the world around you. Notice the details around you. If you are outside, for example, do you see any bugs on the blades of grass or crawling around? Is there a wind? What do you smell? See how long you can sit quietly, simply observing everything around you. How long can you sit? One minute? Three? Five? What do you notice? Did you surprise yourself?

You can write about your experience, draw a picture, or discuss your thoughts with your parents.

Emotional Knowledge

OBJECTIVES

- Discuss feelings and how they affect our lives.
- Review meaning of different feelings words.
- Engage in a cooperative physical activity.
- Stretch imagination.

MATERIALS

Talking stick

Several large sheets of paper

Markers

Stopwatch or watch with second hand

Old magazines (appropriate for participants' age and developmental level)

Scissors

Glue sticks

Copies of the Emotions Vocabulary handout and Home Challenge assignment

Before beginning the session, have someone lie down on a long sheet of paper and trace the outline of the person's body. Draw several body outlines and tape the sheets to the wall on one side of the room.

PROCEDURE

Warm-up

Conduct one of the following warm-ups.

RUBBER BAND STRETCH

Ask participants to spread out around the room. Take participants through the following sequence of stretching and bending several times:

> Stand with your feet flat on the floor and stretch up as high as you
> can. Really try to reach the ceiling! Imagine that you are stretching to

reach one apple at the top of a very tall apple tree, first with one hand, then the other. You've almost got it . . . just a little more. A little more! Now suddenly snap and flop over like a rubber band, touching the floor if you can. Now slowly straighten up, one inch at a time. Slowly . . . feel the bones at the bottom of your back start to straighten . . . now the middle . . . one by one . . . now the top . . . now the neck. Pull up your head last.

STRETCH, SHAKEOUT, FREEZE!

Have each person stand in a different spot in the room with enough space to stretch their arms out to the sides without touching anyone else. Give the instructions "Shake out your hands," "Shake out your arms," "Shake out your shoulders," and so forth. Continue to call out different parts of the body to shake (neck, elbows, knees, ankles, toes, fingers, jaw). You can also ask participants to do two parts at once or shake everything at once. After shaking everything, participants can move about the room shaking everything and also making any additional movements they wish (without touching anyone else). When you call "Freeze!" participants stop immediately and stand still. Freezing means not moving any part of the body, including the mouth or eyes. (Remind participants that they can breathe!) No one is out. Have participants begin moving again. Each time you call "Freeze!" walk around and point out any movements.

Home Challenge Review

Encourage participants to share their responses to the Home Challenge:

- Who was able to do the Home Challenge? What was this like for you?
- What did you notice, sitting quietly?
- What did your senses tell you?
- Did you see anything you didn't see before?
- Did you like this exercise?
- Why or why not?

Discussion

Discuss feelings, emphasizing how they are part of our everyday lives. Talk about how another word for feelings is *emotions*. Sample questions to facilitate discussion include the following:

- What is the difference between thoughts and feelings?
- Do most people like to talk about their feelings? Why or why not?
- How do we show our feelings?
- Why is it important that we show our feelings?
- What things affect how we feel?

- Where in our bodies do we feel different feelings (happiness, anger, curiosity, etc.)?

    If a majority of participants have difficulty distinguishing between thoughts and feelings, it is important to stay with this idea until participants understand it before moving on. When we are asked how we feel, it is sometimes easier to give our thoughts than to say our feelings. For example, if someone asks, "How did you feel?" after a roller coaster ride, the responses "scared" or "excited" are feelings words that describe the emotional experience. The response "I thought I would fall off" or "Like Superman" are thoughts. These responses may imply feelings, but they do not state feelings directly.

Full of Feeling

1. Have participants stand opposite the wall with the body outlines. Give each participant a marker.

2. Tell participants that when you say, "Go!" they should run to the opposite wall and write as many feelings words as they can within the outlines within two minutes.

    If you wish, let participants know that if they list at least 50 words per outline, they will get a special prize, such as stickers or a snack reward to be given at the next session.

3. After two minutes, call time. If after two minutes there are fewer than 20 words on each outline, add another two minutes.

4. Discuss how the emotions participants listed are common to all of us at different times, whether we are aware of them or not. Discuss times we might feel these different emotions.

Emotions Collage

1. Distribute the magazines, scissors, and glue sticks and give each participant a copy of the Emotions Vocabulary list. Invite participants to create a group collage on a large sheet of paper. Instruct them to find magazine pictures that show people expressing different emotions. They can use their list of feelings words as a guide. Challenge participants to find as many different emotions as they can and to fill up the empty space with faces. For fun, they can add different bodies to the faces they pick.

2. Process the collage activity by reviewing the different emotions found. Ask participants: Which emotions were harder to find? Which ones were more common? Hang the collage up in the room in a prominent place.

Wrap-up

1. Discuss session content. Questions to the group could include the following:

    - Were any of the emotions we mentioned today new for you?
    - What was your experience in group today like?

2. Give each participant a copy of the Home Challenge and answer any questions the group might have about the assignment. Remind them that they will have a chance to discuss their responses to the challenge at the beginning of the next session. Be sure to send them home with their Emotions Vocabulary lists as a reference for future Home Challenges. Encourage them to add words to the list whenever they can.

Emotions Vocabulary

Adventurous
Ambivalent
Amused
Angry
Annoyed
Anxious
Apathetic
Apologetic
Ashamed
Awed
Bewildered
Bitter
Bored
Burned out
Calm
Cautious
Cheerful
Compelled
Confident
Confused
Contented
Crabby
Critical
Curious
Depressed
Desperate
Discouraged
Disgruntled
Disgusted
Drained
Ecstatic
Embarrassed
Energized

Enraged
Enthusiastic
Exasperated
Excited
Fed up
Frantic
Frightened
Frustrated
Glad
Gloomy
Grateful
Grim
Guilty
Happy
Helpless
Hopeful
Hurt
Hysterical
Insecure
Inspired
Irritated
Jealous
Joyful
Lonely
Loving
Mad
Melancholy
Mischievous
Miserable
Overwhelmed
Panicky
Peaceful
Proud

Regretful
Rejected
Relaxed
Relieved
Reluctant
Resentful
Restless
Sad
Safe
Scared
Sick
Shy
Skeptical
Smug
Sorry
Spiteful
Surprised
Suspicious
Sympathetic
Tense
Terrified
Thrilled
Tired
Uncertain
Upset
Weary
Wistful
Worried
Wounded

Add your own words:

_____

_____

_____

From *SCIP: Social Competence Intervention Program—A Drama-Based Intervention for Youth on the Autism Spectrum,* © 2008 by L. A. Guli, A. D. Wilkinson, and M. Semrud-Clikeman, Champaign, IL: Research Press (800-519-2707, www.researchpress.com)

Session 3 Home Challenge

Think of a time when you felt these ways:

- Adventurous
- Curious
- Shy

  You can write about your experiences, draw a picture, or discuss your thoughts with your parents.

Session 4

Facial Expressions and Body Language (Part 1)

OBJECTIVES

- Discuss how we know what others are feeling by giving and receiving cues from facial expressions and consider why this is important.
- Experience making a variety of facial expressions and seeing them reflected by others.
- Practice interpreting others' emotions based on their facial cues and body language.
- Practice making a variety of physical movements that express different emotions.
- Discuss how we know what others are feeling by giving and receiving cues from body language and consider why this is important.

MATERIALS

Talking stick

Feelings Cards

Copies of the Home Challenge assignment

> *Before conducting this activity, photocopy the Feelings Cards page and cut apart the words.*

PROCEDURE

Warm-up

> *Conduct the Clones activity (see Session 2 for directions). Repeating this activity links previous experiences with new ones and focuses participants' attention prior to learning new content.*

Home Challenge Review

Encourage participants to share their responses to the Home Challenge.

- Who chose to draw, write, or talk about their experiences?

- Which emotion was the hardest to describe?
- How do you remember expressing how you felt?

Discussion

1. Facilitate a discussion about how facial expression and body language can provide cues about what someone is feeling. For example, you might say:

   How do we know what someone is feeling? Facial expression is one hint, or cue, that gives us an idea. Body language, or how our bodies move, is another. When we communicate, we are giving and taking nonverbal hints, or cues. For example, I might know that someone is feeling angry because their eyebrows are slanting down or because they are frowning or breathing hard or clenching their fists. There are so many different parts of the face, and it can move in so many ways, that even slight changes can change someone's entire expression. Sometimes we have to learn to "read" a face, just as we learn to read a book. Our faces and bodies have a whole other language, a nonverbal one. We're going to practice that language.

2. Choose a group member and invite the group to guess how that person is feeling in that moment, based on their facial expression and body language. Discuss.

Guess the Feeling

1. Have the group sit in a circle. In the middle of the circle, place the stack of Feelings Cards. Each person takes a turn drawing a card and making the facial expression showing that emotion, while the other participants guess what the emotion is.

2. After each participant's turn, ask the following questions:

   - What is it about the expression that shows a certain feeling?
   - What could make the facial expression show the emotion even better?

3. Encourage participants to talk about what it is about the face that expresses the feeling. You might say, for example:

   We can guess that someone might be surprised if their eyes widen, their eyebrows get a little higher, and their mouth opens a little. Maybe even their breathing changes. Sometimes it is hard to define exactly what it is about the face that changes, but identifying different feelings gets easier with practice.

Camera

1. Have the group split into two lines (Line A and Line B), sitting or standing and facing each other about three feet apart. Pick a feeling and ask Line A to think about how to express that feeling.

2. Count backward from five as each person in Line A makes a facial expression to match the feeling. When you get to "one," have the people in Line A "freeze" into

position. Pretend to take their picture. Instruct Line A to stay frozen while participants in Line B examine the expression of the person across from them. Give the people in Line B five seconds to copy the person across from them as best they can.

3. When everyone in Line B has copied the expression of the person across from them in line, pretend to take a picture of Line B.

4. Next name a different emotion. This time, have Line B make facial expressions to reflect the emotion and ask Line A to copy Line B's expressions. Pretend to take each line's picture. Continue the activity as time permits.

Moving with Emotion

1. Have participants spread out around the room. Ask the group to move about in different ways to begin practicing expressing feelings through body language. First have participants bounce, tiptoe, walk in slow motion, walk like giants, and so forth to warm up and get used to moving in different ways.

2. Next ask participants to move around the room as if they are in one of the following situations:

   - You are walking through a haunted house.
   - You just got a test back with a failing grade.
   - The bus is late, and you have to get somewhere on time.
   - You are a very proud king or queen, greeting your subjects.
   - You just found out you won the lottery!
   - You are very bored and don't know what to do.

     This is a silent activity. All emotion must be expressed through facial and body cues. If you wish, call "Freeze" after each situation to regain participants' attention.

3. Have participants return to the sitting circle to process the activity:

   - Did you like the activity? Why or why not?
   - Was it harder or easier to express feelings with body movements or with facial expressions?
   - What did you observe in others?

Wrap-up

1. Discuss session content. Questions to the group could include the following:

   - What activity did you enjoy the most today? Why?
   - Are there other ways to express feelings, besides facial expressions and body language?

2. Give each participant a copy of the Home Challenge and answer any questions the group might have about the assignment. Remind them that they will have a chance to share their responses to the challenge at the beginning of the next session.

Feelings Cards

Happy	Embarrassed
Sad	Hurt
Scared	Relieved
Angry	Surprised
Annoyed	Bored
Excited	Worried

From *SCIP: Social Competence Intervention Program—A Drama-Based Intervention for Youth on the Autism Spectrum,* © 2008 by L. A. Guli, A. D. Wilkinson, and M. Semrud-Clikeman, Champaign, IL: Research Press (800-519-2707, www.researchpress.com)

Session 4 Home Challenge

Turn off the volume for several minutes while you are watching a movie or TV show. What is this like? Can you still tell what's going on? Why or why not? What do you pay attention to? If you have a DVD player or VCR, do this with a scene in a movie that you can watch over again, with and without sound.

You can write about your experience, draw a picture, or discuss your thoughts with your parents.

From *SCIP: Social Competence Intervention Program—A Drama-Based Intervention for Youth on the Autism Spectrum,* © 2008 by L. A. Guli, A. D. Wilkinson, and M. Semrud-Clikeman, Champaign, IL: Research Press (800-519-2707, www.researchpress.com)

Session 5

Facial Expressions and Body Language (Part 2)

OBJECTIVES

- Improve physical control and body awareness through creative movement.
- Continue to discuss strategies for and practice reading nonverbal facial and body language cues.
- Practice reading facial expressions by looking only at the eyes.
- Use imagination in a cooperative activity.

MATERIALS

Talking stick

Feelings Cards (from Session 4) or Emotions Spinwheel

Blank sheet of paper

Copies of the Home Challenge assignment

> *Before beginning this session, photocopy the Emotions Spinwheel, attach it to a sheet of cardboard, and add a spinner (a brad and arrow cut from cardboard work well).*

PROCEDURE

Warm-up

JELLO ROOM

Have participants form a straight line, standing side by side, on one side of the room, then give the following instructions:

> Close your eyes. Imagine that the room in front of you is made of a magic substance that can turn into anything we want it to be. When I say, "Go," the room will no longer be full of air but full of JELLO! Are you ready? OK, open your eyes. The room begins here. (Point to an imaginary wall.) Slowly reach out one finger and touch the Jello. What does it feel like? Put your whole arm in. Feel it all around your arm.

Wiggle it around! Now put your leg in the Jello. Now the other leg! Now your head! OK, now you are free to move about the room. Move around and explore. Remember, the room is full of Jello so you can't move as easily as you would in a normal room. Cross the room and reach the other side. When you get to the end, take each part of your body out of the Jello and shake all the Jello off.

It should take half a minute to a minute for participants to cross the room. Ask participants to go through the room several more times, each time suggesting that the room is made of substances of different textures, such as snow, water, feathers, Superglue, hot caramel, mosquitoes, and so on. Emphasize that each substance would feel different and would cause you to move differently. Participants can help each other get through (or get up) if they get "stuck" in some messy imaginary substance.

If you wish, leaders may join the group in crossing the room.

Home Challenge Review

Encourage participants to share their responses to the Home Challenge:

- When you watched TV or a video with the volume off, what did you watch?
- Could you understand what was happening and how the characters were feeling?
- What clues helped you guess?

Discussion

1. Let participants know that today they will continue to practice reading facial cues and body language. Emphasize that they will now focus on more subtle, difficult-to-read emotions (e.g., curiosity, anxiety, shyness, etc.), feelings that may not be as exaggerated or obvious as expressions of happiness or sadness.

2. By this session, the participants may have formed friendships or begun to have conflicts that present wonderful opportunities for problem-solving in discussion. Remind students about the importance of taking turns and respecting each other.

Reading the Eyes

This activity is basically the same as Guess the Feeling (described in Session 4), but now the participants hold a piece of paper in front of their nose and mouth so that only the eyes can be seen.

1. Ask the group if they have ever heard the expression "The eyes are the windows to the soul." Whether they have or have not, ask them what they think the expression means.

2. Continue by making one of four basic expressions (happy, angry, scared, or sad) with a piece of paper in front of your nose and mouth. Ask if the group can guess what the rest of your face is doing just by looking at the eyes. What is it about the eyes that changes when the expression changes?

3. Give each participant a turn to guess an emotion, as well as a turn to express one, if time permits.

Sculptors and Clay

Have the participants form pairs, or place them in pairs yourself. In this activity, the partners take turns being the "sculptor" and the "clay." The person who is clay begins by crouching on the ground, curled up in a ball. The sculptor then "sculpts" the clay. "Sculpting" refers to gently guiding the person who is the clay into a certain position by taking the person by the hand, shoulders, or touching the person's leg, indicating that it should bend. Ideally, this activity should be done nonverbally so the "clay" must trust the sculptor's intent and take their lead. Ideas for sculptures may include the following:

- Hungry dinosaur
- Tired person climbing a mountain
- Detective solving a crime
- Someone opening up a birthday surprise
- King or queen sitting on a throne
- Rock star in concert

> *If the person who is the clay refuses to be guided by the sculptor, or vice versa, one of the leaders may serve as a substitute in either role. If the problem is in being guided physically, the "clay" can be guided verbally into position.*

Express It!

Have the group make two lines, facing each other. When you say, "Go," one line tries to express a common phrase or statement to the other line using facial expression and body language only. (They cannot mouth it.) Suggestions for phrases include the following:

- Help!
- I'm sorry.
- You're kidding!
- I don't believe you.
- Listen to me!
- I'm exhausted.
- Thank you.

> *It is important to take time to discuss what feelings are often associated with these phrases ("Thank you" = gratitude, "You're kidding" = surprise, "Listen to me!" = frustration, "Help!" = fear, and so on.)*

Wrap-up

1. Discuss session content. Questions to the group could include the following:

   - For some people, expressing feelings is easier. For others, "reading" or guessing them is easier. What is your experience?
   - Which activity was the most helpful for you today?

2. Give each participant a copy of the Home Challenge and answer any questions the group might have about the assignment. Remind them that they will have a chance to share their responses to the challenge at the beginning of the next session.

Session 5 Home Challenge

If you have the opportunity, teach your mom or dad one of the activities we have done so far, then think about what this experience was like for you.

You can write about your experience, draw a picture, or discuss your thoughts with your parents.

Session 6

Vocal Cues

OBJECTIVES

- Experiment with using vocal expression in different ways in front of peers.
- Discuss how people express feelings by their tone of voice.
- Practice saying the same sentence with a variety of emotions.
- Practice saying the same sentence with emphasis on different words.

MATERIALS

Talking stick

A copy of the Say It with Feeling Sentences

Container

Feelings Cards (Session 4) or Emotions Spinwheel (Session 5)

Copies of the Home Challenge assignment

Tape recorder and audiotape *(optional)*

> *Before conducting this activity, photocopy the Say It with Feeling Sentences and put them in the container for participants to draw.*

> *If you wish, audiotape participants and play their voices back so they can hear themselves speaking in different ways in the Say It with Feelings and Stress It activities.*

PROCEDURE

Warm-up

SLOW-MOTION FREEZE TAG

This is actually the traditional game of freeze tag, but players move in slow motion. The player who is "It" chases people and tags them, making them freeze in place. Other players must reach their frozen teammates and "untag" them before they are tagged themselves. Remind participants to move as slowly as possible. If there is enough space, you may want to switch from playing the game in slow motion to playing it at normal speed when players least expect it. In a different and slightly more complex version of this game, the person who is "It" freezes after tagging another person, who then becomes the new "It." In this version, one by one, all players are eventually frozen.

Home Challenge Review

Encourage participants to share their responses to the Home Challenge:

- Did you have a chance to teach your parents an activity? If so, how did it go?
- If your parents were too busy to do the activity, how could you let them know that this would be important to you?

> *Let group members know that it's OK if they didn't have a chance to do the activity—or if it felt strange to do an activity with their mom or dad.*

Discussion

1. Explain that today the group will focus on how to tell what someone is feeling from the way their voice sounds. Facilitate a discussion about how vocal cues such as tone and rhythm can provide cues about what someone is feeling. For example, you can ask the group how someone's voice can tell us what a person is feeling, then say something like the following:

   > Vocal tone and rhythm are some cues that can give us an idea. Just like with facial expression and body language, we can get some cues if we pay very close attention. For example, I might know that someone is feeling excited or sad if they are speaking in a certain *tone of voice*. Who has heard that expression before? What do you think it means? When we speak, our voice goes up and down, and changes, like music. Sometimes it is higher, sometimes lower—sometimes faster, sometimes slower. Sometimes the rhythm or beat changes. All of these changes in our voice can help express feelings. We can learn to "read" or hear a voice better, just like we are practicing reading faces. It is all part of the nonverbal language that we are learning to understand.

2. Point out that there are many things about the way we speak that express the feelings behind the words and the meanings we want to show. If we think about what someone says and how the person's voice sounds separately, it can make it easier to understand what they mean and how they feel.

Sound Circle

This activity is similar to the Name Game, described in Session 1, except that instead of saying their names, group members take turns making a creative noise with a creative movement. For example, the first person may raise their hands high and say, "Whoop!" or turn around twice and say, "Swish." After the first person, the group repeats all the movements and sounds from the beginning, adding the most recent one.

Say It with Feeling

1. Have participants sit in a circle. Each participant and leader draws a different sentence from the container.

2. A leader then draws a Feelings Card or spins the Emotions Spinwheel and reads his or her sentence with the emotion shown on the card or wheel. For example, if the leader draws the word *happy*, he or she reads the sentence in a happy way. Participants then read the sentences they have drawn in a happy way.

3. After going around the circle once, with group members saying the different sentences with one emotion, the leader chooses another Feelings Card or spins again for a different emotion (e.g., *sad*), and participants repeat the process by reading their sentences with that emotion.

4. After at least four or five emotions have gone around the circle, process the activity by asking the participants how their sentence changed when read each time with a different emotion. The following questions may help:

   - What made the sentences sound different?
   - Did the sound go up or down at the end of the sentence?
   - Were the words loud or soft?
   - Did rhythm have something to do with the feeling expressed?
   - How did the meaning of the sentences change?

     This activity is likely to lead to some laughing because the sentences really sound different and imply different meanings when read with different emotions.

Sound Effects

1. Have participants choose partners or assign partners yourself.

2. Give the following instructions:

   Partner A moves randomly around the room, making interesting movements and not making physical contact with anyone else. As A moves, B follows directly behind. B does not copy A's movements, but instead makes sounds that go with the movements. Partner B tries to support Partner A's motion with sound until it seems they are united rather than two people doing separate things.

3. After the A's have had a chance to lead, instruct partners to switch roles.

4. Briefly process the activity with the following questions:

   - How did you know what noises to make to go with the movements?
   - What cues did you get from your partner?
   - Why might some sounds and movements seem to "go together" more than others?

Stress It

1. Say a sentence several times. Each time you do it, put the emphasis on a different word. Have participants close their eyes and try to pick out the word that is emphasized. For example:

   > *I* can do that. (Implies that I can, but maybe somebody else can't.)
   >
   > I *can* do that. (Implies it is possible.)
   >
   > I can do *that.* (Implies that I can do that particular thing.)

2. When participants get used to this idea, give each person a turn to say the sample sentence three times, with emphasis on a different word each time. They can then take turns putting emphasis on each word in the sentence "I want it now."

3. Discuss why emphasis and/or inflection on different words may produce different meanings. Encourage participants to practice listening for the stress on different words.

   > *This may be difficult for participants since they already said sentences differently through voice intonation in the Say It with Feeling game. This time, however, they are to change the meaning of the sentence with emphasis and accent on a specific word rather than vocal tone. Both skills are a part of prosody.*

Wrap-up

1. Discuss the session content. Questions to the group could include "Is it harder to pay attention to vocal cues or facial cues?" (In other words, is it harder to hear emotion in people's voices or to see it in their facial expressions and body language?)

2. Give each participant a copy of the Home Challenge and answer any questions the group might have about the assignment. Remind them that they will have a chance to share their responses to the challenge at the beginning of the next session.

Say It with Feeling Sentences

Mary had a little lamb.	Come with me.
The house is flooded with chocolate.	I had an interesting dream last night.
May the force be with you.	It's over.
Let's go shopping.	That smells great.
I want to go home.	School's closed today?
It's all right.	I want to go, too!
That's impossible.	Whatever.
It sounds really great.	It's snowing.
I love you.	Don't worry about it. I'm OK.

From *SCIP: Social Competence Intervention Program—A Drama-Based Intervention for Youth on the Autism Spectrum,* © 2008 by L. A. Guli, A. D. Wilkinson, and M. Semrud-Clikeman, Champaign, IL: Research Press (800-519-2707, www.researchpress.com)

Emotions Spinwheel

Make the spinwheel from card stock, using a brad to attach the "spinner." If you wish, make the slice for each word a different color. Feel free to substitute different words if the words in this example are too basic.

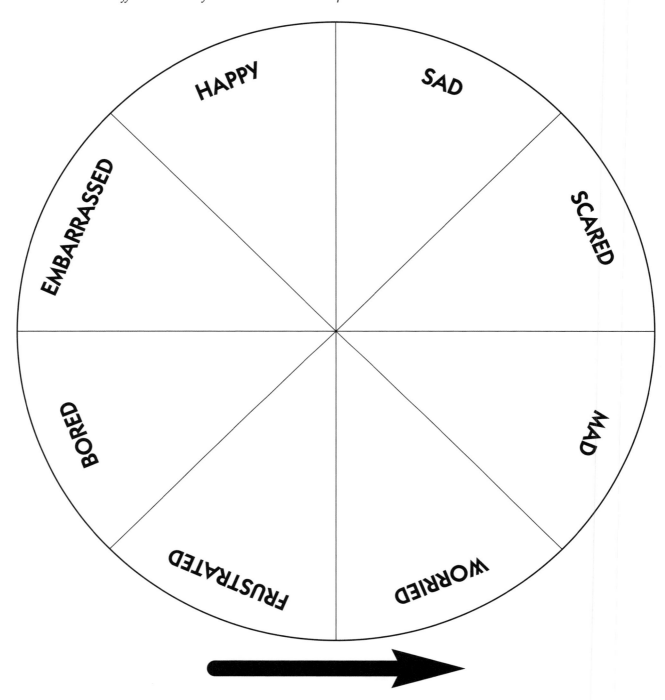

Session 6 Home Challenge

Practice saying the following sentence with a parent or another family member by putting the emphasis on a different word each time:

"I like you."

Talk to your family member about what gives the sentence a different meaning each time. Then ask your family member to say the sentence to you with the emphasis on a different word each time.

- Is it funny to do this?

- Can you tell how saying the sentence differently changes the meaning?

If a family member is not available to do this, maybe you can tape yourself saying the sentence in the different ways and then listen to the recording of your own voice.

You can write about your experience, draw a picture, or discuss your thoughts with your parents.

From *SCIP: Social Competence Intervention Program—A Drama-Based Intervention for Youth on the Autism Spectrum,* © 2008 by L. A. Guli, A. D. Wilkinson, and M. Semrud-Clikeman, Champaign, IL: Research Press (800-519-2707, www.researchpress.com)

Session 7

Putting Cues Together

OBJECTIVES

- Discuss what communicating successfully means in real life—figuring out facial expression, voice, and body language at the same time.
- Express and interpret visual and auditory cues together in cooperative activities.
- Engage in more complex improvisational activities with a partner.
- Take the risk of sounding silly in front of peers by speaking in "Babble."

MATERIALS

Talking stick

Copies of the Home Challenge assignment

PROCEDURE

Warm-up

BUBBLE GUM

One person is chosen to be the "bubble gum." While everyone else closes their eyes, the bubble gum finds a place in the room to stand silently. The object of the game is for players to find the bubble gum and stick to this person. When you say, "Go," players begin to walk around the room carefully, keeping their eyes closed, trying to find the bubble gum. When they touch or bump into another person, they must say, "Bubble gum." If the person they touch replies, "Bubble gum," then they know that they have NOT found the bubble gum and must keep moving. If they say, "Bubble gum" and get no response, they know that they have found the bubble gum (made up of one or more people who have also found bubble gum). At that point, they open their eyes and stick to the gum. The game continues until all players are stuck together. Players can get a hint about where the bubble gum might be by listening to the other players.

Home Challenge Review

Encourage participants to share their responses to the Home Challenge. Ask:

- How did practicing the sentence with your mom or dad go?

- Could you hear when they put the stress on a different word?
- Could they tell when you did?

Discussion

Discuss putting facial, voice, and body cues together with context. To begin, you might say something like this:

> We've talked about strategies for figuring out what people are feeling or intending by looking at their faces and body movements, as well as their voices. It's time to put them all together! This can be a little complicated at times because sometimes interactions between people happen very fast and more than one thing is going on at once. Sometimes one cue holds more information than another. Paying close attention to all of the nonverbal cues can help us understand someone's intentions better.

Tower of Babble

1. Explain that participants will learn to talk in "Babble," a made-up language. Everyone should talk as if making perfect sense, using as many sounds as possible and exaggerating mouth movements (for example, don't say, "Blah, blah, blah," but use a mixture of syllables, such as "Plintera frington globby foo").

2. Pair up participants and give them two or three of the following topics of conversation to discuss in Babble:

   - Describe your favorite movie to each other.
   - Describe your favorite food to each other.
   - Tell your partner about the scariest dream you ever had.
   - Pretend you have a very exciting secret and are dying to tell someone.

3. If participants pick up on this activity quickly, do the following variation. First, ask them to begin the conversation in English. At some point in the conversation, ask them to switch to Babble. Remind them to listen to each other, to take turns talking, and, especially, to pay close attention to the expressions and tone of voice used by the speaker to help them know how to respond.

4. Afterward, have a brief discussion. Ask participants, "How did you know how to respond when you didn't understand any of the words?"

   In addition to helping participants interpret nonverbal cues, conversing in Babble helps them adapt to role-playing without feeling so self-conscious. Babble may be hard for participants who think that they have to do it "right" or are afraid of sounding silly, so be very encouraging. Join in the conversations if you wish.

Birthday Gifts

1. Have participants take different partners than in the previous activity so that they have an opportunity to interact with other group members. Let them know that they will take turns pretending that they are giving and receiving gifts. The giver can choose to give the receiver anything, no matter what size or how ridiculous (an elephant, an empty box, a piece of used chewing gum, etc.). The challenge for the recipient is to accept every gift with great enthusiasm. The giver may or may not tell the receiver what the gift is.

2. Before having participants begin, model as silly an exchange as you can. For example:

   Leader 1: I've decided to get you a present.

   Leader 2: A present? For me? That's wonderful!

   Leader 1: I'm going to bring it in, but it's a little difficult. *(Pantomime dragging in something large on a long rope.)* OK. It's in! It's a giant stuffed polar bear! What do you think?

   Leader 2: Um . . . um . . . I LOVE it! It's beautiful, it's . . . Thank you SO MUCH! Wow!

   Leader 1: Oh, it's nothing. I wanted to get you something special.

   Leader 2: No, no, really, you shouldn't have! I'm so touched, it's the best present I ever got.

Wrap-up

1. Discuss session content. Praise participants for having the courage to be silly and take risks in front of each other, as well as for working so well together. Questions to the group could include the following:

   - Did talking in Babble help you express emotions?
   - How did you know what to say in the Babble activity?
   - What cues did you look for?
   - How were you a helpful partner today?

2. Give each participant a copy of the Home Challenge and answer any questions the group might have about the assignment. Remind them that they will have a chance to share responses to the challenge at the beginning of the next session.

Session 7 Home Challenge

Be on the lookout for a situation in which you don't know what someone really means or how they feel. In this situation, how did you think the person felt? Why do you think the person felt this way?

You can write about your experience, draw a picture, or discuss your thoughts with your parents.

From *SCIP: Social Competence Intervention Program—A Drama-Based Intervention for Youth on the Autism Spectrum,* © 2008 by L. A. Guli, A. D. Wilkinson, and M. Semrud-Clikeman, Champaign, IL: Research Press (800-519-2707, www.researchpress.com)

Sessions 8 and 9

When Cues Don't Match

Process drama is introduced in this session. Instructions for two process dramas, "Detective Agency" and "Edna Snipes," are given in the appendix. In these dramas, participants play the part of detectives attempting to solve a mystery. You may do both dramas, one in Session 8 and the other in Session 9, or you may conduct a single drama over two sessions if you feel your group needs more time.

OBJECTIVES

- Experience being "in role" in a process drama.
- Build upon the ideas of others in a cooperative activity.
- Practice making decisions in a group.
- Discuss and practice situations in which visual and auditory cues don't match or when visual or auditory cues don't match context cues.
- Develop strategies for dealing with ambiguous situations.

MATERIALS

Talking stick

Props and other materials for the process drama(s) chosen (listed in the appendix with the dramas)

Copies of the Home Challenge assignment

PROCEDURE

Warm-ups

"YES, AND . . ."

The group sits in a circle, and a leader says a sentence to begin a story. Each person takes a turn adding an idea to the sentence. Each new idea must build on the idea of the previous person and not contradict it in any way. The sentences don't need to make a whole lot of sense; however, they must logically follow the preceding ones. For example, if you start with "I think it would be really fun to go camping," the next person can say, "Yes, and we can go fishing for barracuda," while the next adds, "Yes, and then we can eat them for dinner."

This activity practices building on the cues of others and working coopera-
tively. (If it's around Halloween, you can make this activity a ghost story —
turn the lights off and pass around a flashlight.)

WHAT COULD IT BE?

Participants and group leaders sit in a circle. A common object, such as a pen or a shoe, is placed in the middle. Group leaders explain that the goal is to imagine how to use the object in as many ways as possible. For example, a group leader walks to the middle of the circle, picks up a pen, and pantomines using it as a comb, a computer keyboard, or a piece of corn on the cob. Participants then guess what the original object represents. Each person gets a turn. This activity is an effective way to encourage flexible thinking and expand imagination.

Home Challenge Review

Encourage participants to share their responses to the Home Challenge:

- What situations did you encounter when you didn't know what someone meant or how they felt?
- What did you do?

Discussion

1. Ask participants to reflect back on the Say It with Feeling game from Session 6. You might say:

   During the game, sometimes the cues didn't really match. Have you ever seen someone say, "I'm fine" with a smile, but something about the person's voice seemed to say the opposite? Sometimes a person's voice might match the words, but the facial expression doesn't. And sometimes neither the person's voice nor facial expression matches the words.

2. Point out that the *context,* or what is actually happening in the situation, is important in figuring out what is meant. Ask:

   - When might someone be saying something in one way and meaning something else?
   - How can you use what is happening in a situation to help you know what the person really means?
   - Why is it important to figure out what someone means?

3. Encourage participants to brainstorm strategies they might use when it is unclear what someone means. Responses might include the following:

   - Use context cues.
   - Ask the person what he or she means.
   - Choose one cue over another if it feels more genuine.

- Make a judgment based on a past experience.
- Take some time to process the situation—don't react immediately.

Process Dramas: Detective Agency/Edna Snipes

Conduct the process drama or dramas you have chosen, following the instructions given in the appendix.

> *Feel free to adapt the dramas in terms of difficulty: Adding suspects, discovering contradictory evidence, changing the intensity of the suspects' nonverbal cues, and even creating a conspiracy between two guilty suspects can create more of a challenge for advanced detectives.*

> *You may substitute the optional activities on the next page if you feel that these dramas are too complex for your group. You could also add these activities at this or another time to reinforce the concepts.*

Wrap-up

1. Discuss what the participants learned today and what the experience of solving a mystery was like for them. Sample questions for the group include the following:

   - What was your favorite part of the drama? Why?
   - What was the most difficult part of the drama?
   - When were times while you were solving the mystery today that you needed to use a strategy to help you tell what someone meant?
   - Did anyone learn a new strategy today to use when cues don't match? Did your strategy work?

2. Give each participant a copy of the Home Challenge and answer any questions the group might have about the assignment. Remind them that they will have a chance to discuss their responses to the challenge at the beginning of the next session.

Optional Activities

WITCH AT THE DOOR

The group is seated in a circle, in discussion, when they hear a knock on the door. A group leader answers the door to find another group leader, or guest, dressed up as a famous scary fairy tale or story character (e.g., a witch). The character is very distressed because he or she has been horribly misunderstood. Everyone the witch meets is either mean or runs away scared! This character takes a seat in the middle of the circle and is interviewed by group members. Group members attempt to find out what the character is really all about, what the character wants, and what the character really feels. For instance, the witch might act scary because he or she is nervous meeting people or has a stutter. The witch might want to be friends with people but just not know how to behave appropriately. The conversation might go something like this:

> **Witch:** *(Frowning, looking mean)* I don't know why no one wants to play with me!
>
> **Participant:** You're a little . . . scary.
>
> **Witch:** *(Turns and shouts at participant)* Scary? How?
>
> **Group leader:** Can anyone think of a reason?
>
> **Participant:** Well, she's yelling. And her face looks mad.
>
> **Witch:** *(Still frowning, with brows furrowed)* What looks mad about it? I'm as friendly as can be!

> *The conversation continues as the participants teach the witch how she can be more approachable to others.*

PET DETECTIVE

The leader introduces himself or herself as an agent from the Animal Division of the FBI. The agent has learned that the participants are all talented detectives, especially when it comes to figuring out what others might be saying through their nonverbal cues. The agent needs their help: Can they offer their assistance in solving a baffling case? The division has received a call from the First Lady about the President's missing dog. At 1:00 P.M., an aide went to get the leash to give the First Pooch a walk. All she found was a broken dog treat and a brief ransom note. It read, "Mr. President, we have your dog. If you want him back, leave $100,000 in a paper bag on the blue bench in the park.

There is, thankfully, one witness—a gardener who happened to see the dognapper running out of the house with the dog under his arm. The gardener tried to stop the thief, but the gardener's lame leg prevented him from running very far. Overcome with grief since he helped raise the dog from a puppy, the gardener is unable to explain what happened and has been reduced to speaking in Babble (see Session 7 for details).

> *The leader appeals to the participants for help: Can they help decipher what happened through the gardener's tone of voice and nonverbal cues?*

Session 8 Home Challenge

Sometimes nonverbal cues don't match because a person is lying, as is the case in our drama. Sometimes there are other reasons their cues might not match. What might some other reasons be?

You can write your response, draw a picture, or discuss your thoughts with your parents.

Session 9 Home Challenge

What was it like being in role today? Did you enjoy pretending that you were someone else? How did you feel? Did acting with others help you in any way?

You can write your response, draw a picture, or discuss your thoughts with your parents.

From *SCIP: Social Competence Intervention Program—A Drama-Based Intervention for Youth on the Autism Spectrum,* © 2008 by L. A. Guli, A. D. Wilkinson, and M. Semrud-Clikeman, Champaign, IL: Research Press (800-519-2707, www.researchpress.com)

Session 10

Point of View

This session introduces the "Standing in Someone Else's Shoes" process drama (see instructions in the appendix). In this drama, participants take on the roles of talk show guests—who hold different opinions—and the show's audience members.

OBJECTIVES

- Discuss the difference between facts and opinions.
- Discuss what it means to think and see from another person's point of view or perspective.
- Express personal points of view.
- Accept others' points of view that are different from one's own.
- Argue from different points of view about various subjects.

MATERIALS

Talking stick

Paper, pencil, and clipboard for each participant

A large stuffed animal (or another large object)

Large index cards with the words *FACT* and *OPINION* written on them

Three signs, reading *Strongly Agree, Strongly Disagree,* and *Somewhere in the Middle*

Dictionary

Props and other materials for the process drama (listed in the appendix)

Copies of the Home Challenge assignment

PROCEDURE

Warm-up

POINT OF VIEW DRAWINGS

Place a large stuffed animal or another large object in the center of the room. Provide a pencil, several pieces of paper, and a clipboard for each participant. As participants enter, give them the drawing materials. Direct them to sit in different places around the room to draw the object. Every two minutes, ask them to move to a different spot and draw the object again from their new perspective.

Home Challenge Review

Session 8

Encourage participants to share their responses to the Session 8 Home Challenge.

- Could you think of any other reasons (besides lying) that nonverbal cues (from face, voice, and body language) might not match?
- In the situation you described, what would be the most helpful cue for you to focus on?

Session 9

Encourage participants to share their responses to the Session 9 Home Challenge:

- Are you looking forward to being "in role" again?
- What was easy or challenging about it?

Discussion

1. Ask the group what they think *point of view* is and process different responses. Explain that because different people have had different experiences, they have different opinions. Another way of saying that people have different opinions is that people have different points of view, or perspectives, about things. Explain that, just as the object participants were drawing appeared different from different parts of the room, each of us experiences or sees a situation differently.

2. Ask:

- When are times when we might try to see from another person's point of view?
- Why is it important to see from someone else's point of view?

Fact versus Opinion

It may be necessary for your group to discuss the difference between fact and opinion. You may wish to do the following brief activity to review these concepts and use a dictionary to define these terms. It's also helpful to have a dictionary on hand to look up any unknown words ("feline," for example).

1. Ask participants to explain how the concepts of *fact* and *opinion* are different, in their own words.

2. Give several facts and opinions, in random order. After each statement, encourage the group to shout out which they think each statement is. After they do so, hold up the *FACT* or *OPINION* card, whichever is correct. If participants disagree, allow them to explain why.

Facts

    The earth is round.

    Cats belong to the species *feline*.

    There are human beings in this room right now.

    We live in the United States of America.

Opinions

    Spinach tastes bad.

    Everyone should go to church.

    The president is a funny man.

    Television is good for you.

Where Do You Stand?

Post each of the three signs in a different part of the room.

Explain that another way of describing someone's opinion is to use the expression "where a person stands." Tell the group that they will express some of their own points of view by voting with their feet. You will read several statements: If participants strongly agree with the statement, they will go and stand next to the *Strongly Agree* sign; if not, they will stand next to the *Strongly Disagree* sign. If they both agree a little and disagree a little, they stand by the *Somewhere in the Middle* sign. Sample statements:

- Pizza is a healthy food to eat.
- Boys and girls are equal.
- Video games are bad.
- School is fun.
- It is good to exercise two hours a day.
- Video games encourage violence.
- Dogs are better than cats.
- We should always tell the truth.

    Because this activity intends to elicit differences, it may result in conflict between participants. If conflict occurs, welcome it and use it as an opportunity for discussion. Older participants may note that different interpretations of words (e.g., the word "equal") may cause people to answer differently.

Process Drama: Standing In Someone Else's Shoes

Conduct the process drama, following the instructions provided in the appendix. (Since the session is quite full, the process drama might have to be extended to the next session.)

Wrap-up

1. Discuss the session content. Questions to the group could include the following:

    *   Sometimes it's hard to accept that someone has a different opinion than you do. Why is it important to learn to do this?
    *   What was it like to argue from two different points of view?
    *   Did any of the activities help you see from someone else's point of view today?

2. Choose one of the two Home Challenge options provided. Give each participant a copy of the challenge and answer any questions the group might have about the assignment. Remind them that they will have a chance to discuss their responses to the challenge at the beginning of the next session.

Session 10 Home Challenge (Option 1)

Imagine the story of Cinderella or Shrek told from a different point of view.

- What would the story of Cinderella be like if told from the point of view of one of the stepsisters?
- What would Shrek's story be like if Lord Farquaad told it?

  You can write your response, draw a picture, or discuss your thoughts with your parents.

From *SCIP: Social Competence Intervention Program—A Drama-Based Intervention for Youth on the Autism Spectrum,* © 2008 by L. A. Guli, A. D. Wilkinson, and M. Semrud-Clikeman, Champaign, IL: Research Press (800-519-2707, www.researchpress.com)

Session 10 Home Challenge (Option 2)

With your parents' permission, watch a real talk show that invites several different guests. Notice the different points of view on the show and why people may have a hard time understanding one another's positions.

You can write about your experience, draw a picture, or discuss your thoughts with your parents.

Session 11

Understanding Interactions (Part 1)

In this session, participants take part in one of two process dramas—"Space Mission" or "Advertising Agency"—as described in the appendix. The circumstances of these dramas establish the need for participants to create a videorecording of typical social interactions in which nonverbal cues play an essential part. In Session 12, participants have the opportunity to record these situations, then view and give feedback on them.

OBJECTIVES

- Work cooperatively with others to complete a project.
- Practice using nonverbal cues in typical peer interactions.
- Help one another break these interactions down in a step-by-step fashion.
- Learn to give and receive feedback from each other regarding nonverbal cues.

MATERIALS

Talking stick

Props and other materials for the process drama chosen (listed in the appendix with the dramas)

Copies of the Home Challenge assignment

PROCEDURE

Warm-up

Follow the instructions given in Session 7 for the Babble activity. Do one conversation only. Repeating this activity will help carry over concepts from the previous sessions and loosen inhibitions.

Home Challenge Review

Encourage participants to share their responses to the Home Challenge.

Option 1

- Who imagined a story told from a different point of view? Tell us what you imagined.
- How is the story you imagined different from the original?

Option 2

- Who watched a talk show? What did you notice?
- Were the guests on the show able to learn about each others' points of view or not?
- Were you able to see both points of view? If so, what helped you?

Process Dramas: Space Mission/Advertising Agency

Conduct the process drama of your choice, following the instructions given in the appendix. The Advertising Agency drama may be more appropriate for older participants. Although it may not be as "flashy" as Space Mission, it can be just as fun and engaging.

> *If time permits, you may begin the process of choosing, rehearsing, and recording the interactions associated with the drama, as described in Session 12.*

Wrap-up

1. Discuss the session content. Questions to the group could include the following:

   - Did the activities today help you understand more about taking another person's point of view or having different perspectives? Why or why not?
   - Do you think there is always one "right" person and one "wrong" person in a story?
   - Does knowing more about what someone else has experienced change your ideas?

2. Give each participant a copy of the Home Challenge and answer any questions the group might have about the assignment. Remind them that they will have a chance to discuss their responses to the challenge at the beginning of the next session.

Session 11 Home Challenge

Can you think of times in your life when you have to work with others? What is the best thing about working with other people? What is the most difficult thing?

You can write about your experience, draw a picture, or discuss your thoughts with your parents.

Session 12

Understanding Interactions (Part 2)

OBJECTIVES

- Work cooperatively to choose, develop, and make videorecordings of situations involving important nonverbal content.
- Observe one's own and others' interactions on the videorecordings and reflect about how they might appear to others.
- Give and receive feedback about the use of nonverbal communication in social interactions.

MATERIALS

Talking stick

Props and other materials (depending on the process drama chosen and the interactions participants choose to enact)

Video camera and monitor or screen for playback

Copies of the Home Challenge assignment

PROCEDURE

Warm-up

ROLE SPOTLIGHTING

Have participants spread out throughout the room and close their eyes. If you are conducting the Space Mission drama, ask them to imagine that it is a typical day in a space station and that they are beginning the day's jobs. Guide participants to open their eyes and, remaining where they are, pantomime the kinds of activities that their unique character would do on the space station (e.g., making breakfast, speaking with mission control, mapping stars, fixing electronics, talking to other planets, etc.). If you are conducting the Advertising Agency activity, have them pantomime writing, fixing a computer, talking on the phone, giving a presentation, and so forth. For either activity, "spotlight" the participants one by one, asking them to pantomime their action and then describe their character's job to the group.

Home Challenge Review

Encourage participants to share their responses to the Home Challenge:

- What was it like for you to think about times when you had to work with others?
- What are some of your experiences working with others?

Process Dramas (Continued from Session 11)

GENERATING AND DEVELOPING THE SITUATIONS

Participants next brainstorm about the types of scenes they would like to record. Group leaders help the participants develop their ideas. Ideally, the scenes are suggested and developed by participants. However, some possible situations to choose from—appropriate for either drama—appear on page 121. The group chooses three or four situations that they believe will best represent how nonverbal aspects of communication work in human interactions.

ENACTING AND RECORDING THE SITUATIONS

Leaders next divide participants into groups of two, three, or more (depending on the scene) and instruct them to improvise their scenes. They may practice their scenes once or twice. Then, with the leaders' help, they verbalize what is happening "nonverbally." Leaders coach them on how to break down the interaction down step by step, verbalizing the nonverbal cues they are using to read another person's emotions or intent.

For example, in the Space Mission process drama, participants could choose to act out a situation in which someone is looking sad and someone else approaches and tries to comfort the person. (In the following scene, MeeTu is a space alien central to the story.) The improvisation might go like this:

Group Leader: Action!

> *Johnny sits on the floor, looking sad. Freddy walks by, sees Johnny, and stops.*

Freddy: What's wrong?

Johnny: I tried out for the basketball team, but I didn't make it.

Freddy: (*Puts his hand on Johnny's shoulder.*) Do you want to read a comic together with me?

Johnny: (*Smiling*) OK.

> *The two sit down to read together.*

Group Leader: Cut! Great job acting it out! Now let's see if we can explain the situation to MeeTu and his friends. Johnny, first tell MeeTu and his people what this scene was about.

Johnny: Well, I was feeling sad because something bad happened, and then a friend came over and tried to make me feel better.

Group Leader: Can you explain how you acted out being sad?

Johnny: I pretended to cry.

MeeTu: *Cry* is the word for H_2O leaking out of the eyes, yes?

Johnny: Yeah.

MeeTu: You did some other strange things, too.

Group Leader: Johnny, what are some other things you did to try and look sad?

Johnny: I was frowning.

MeeTu: Yes, the corners of the mouth were down.

Group Leader: Great! Now let's see if Freddy can explain how he acted concerned.

Johnny: He patted me on the shoulder!

Freddy: I tried to wrinkle my forehead, too.

MeeTu: I saw the lines on the forehead. Humans do that often.

Freddy: And my voice was soft, and I made it go up at the end like a question, and I tried to walk up to him real quiet, and I tried to think if he was my friend what would I do . . .

Group Leader: Great job, Freddy! You did a lot of things to look concerned! Is there anything else we should know about your scene?

Freddy: I don't think so.

MeeTu: One thing I do not understand: Why was Johnny's mouth and face all turned up at the end?

Freddy: I smiled then because I saw that he was trying to help me feel better, and it made me happy.

Group Leader: Great! How about we do the scene again and then explain what's happening, just like you did, but on camera this time for MeeTu's people?

Group leaders can ask the following specific questions to help participants explain the nonverbal cues in their scene:

- What is happening in this scene?
- What was your character feeling?
- How did you show it?
- What was your face doing?
- What was the tone of your voice?
- What was your body doing?
- What were the words saying?

WATCHING AND GIVING FEEDBACK ABOUT THE SCENES

Once all the scenes have been recorded, leaders play the scenes for everyone to watch before the recording is sent to the alien world (or to In-Touch Publishing, in the case of the Advertising Agency process drama). One of the most useful aspects of this session is that participants have the opportunity to view themselves on the recording, and in doing so, gain insights about themselves and how they are perceived.

It is important for participants to give and receive constructive feedback about what they perceive in others' scenes and what they meant to communicate in their own. After the participants watch a scene, they discuss how they are communicating through nonverbal cues and how these cues are interpreted. Leaders pause the recording at important moments to discuss expressions or gestures that are incongruous, overexaggerated, or too subtle. Consider this example from the Space Mission drama:

> Astronaut Smith, look at your face in this scene. In the situation, you are supposed to be irritated, but your face doesn't look irritated to me. We need to show what an irritated face looks like. Try looking irritated right now, and maybe the other group members can help you make your face look irritated.

> *At this point in the intervention, leaders will know participants well enough to know who needs to work on having a more expressive face, who needs to modulate their voice tone, and so forth. As you give feedback to the participants, make sure to choose "teachable moments" from the recordings that resemble the social output difficulties the participants exhibit in real life, rather than problems with their acting abilities.*

Finally, group leaders ask the participants if they have any reactions to seeing themselves on the recording. Do they appear different than they expected? If so, how?

Wrap-up

1. Discuss the session content. Questions to the group could include the following:

   - What was it like seeing yourself on the recording today? Did anything surprise you?
   - What did you learn by watching yourself?
   - Did you receive any useful feedback from others?
   - Did your feedback help others in the group understand things in a better way?

   In particular, the discussion should focus on how it felt to try to teach the nonverbal component of social interactions to someone else.

2. Give each participant a copy of the Home Challenge and answer any questions the group might have about the assignment. Remind them that they will have a chance to discuss their responses to the challenge at the beginning of the next session.

Suggested Situations

If you wish, you can photocopy this page and cut the situations apart, then have participants draw them from a hat.

1. Someone wants to play a game with you and you don't feel like playing; you are reading a book.

2. You have to tell your friend that you broke his or her favorite game.

3. You got a better grade on your English test than your best friend did. You brag about it.

4. Someone is looking sad, and another participant tries to comfort the person.

5. On the playground, one person won't let another play catch.

6. A mother and a father tell their son that they are moving to another country.

7. A teenager gets a pierced ear and comes home to unhappy parents.

8. Walking down the street, two people bump into each other. After a moment, they realize that they are old friends from years ago and are very excited to see each other.

9. You are over at your friend's house for dinner. His mom cooks something, but you don't really like it.

10. Two girls are gossiping about another girl who walks up and overhears them.

11. Two people are watching a really funny movie. One person is laughing so hard that he spills popcorn over the other one.

12. It is your mom's or dad's birthday, and you made them something special. You really hope they like it.

13. You are very frustrated because you can't figure out a math problem. A friend comes along and offers to help you.

14. You are standing in line, and someone cuts in front of you.

From *SCIP: Social Competence Intervention Program—A Drama-Based Intervention for Youth on the Autism Spectrum,* © 2008 by L. A. Guli, A. D. Wilkinson, and M. Semrud-Clikeman, Champaign, IL: Research Press (800-519-2707, www.researchpress.com)

Session 12 Home Challenge

Use your imagination to think of what will happen when you send off your scenes of different social interactions. How will your scenes help explain nonverbal behavior?

You can write your response, draw a picture, or discuss your thoughts with your parents.

Session 13

Becoming Fluent in Conversation

If you need more time to complete the Space Mission or Advertising Agency process dramas, this session can be eliminated, or the session's activities can be combined with Sessions 14 and 15.

OBJECTIVES

- Discuss things that prevent us from initiating conversation.
- Increase self-confidence about initiating conversation.
- Practice initiating and making conversation.
- Develop cognitive strategies for combating negative self-talk about reaching out to others.
- Discuss appropriate and inappropriate times to initiate conversation.
- Interpret metaphorical statements.

MATERIALS

Two chairs

A microphone (toy or real)

Copies of the Home Challenge assignment

PROCEDURE

Warm-up

EXPERT

Participants take turns talking on a topic that they don't know much about. Each group member stands in front of the group with the microphone and pretends to be an expert on a subject chosen by the group leaders (e.g., dogs, a popular TV show, the planet Mars). Each participant has one minute to say as much as possible. (It doesn't have to be true!) The object is to talk as much as possible without pausing or saying "Um" or "Uh." If a participant does pause or say "Um" or "Uh," he or she sits down and lets someone else try. Each participant has a turn.

Home Challenge Review

Encourage participants to share their responses to the Home Challenge:

- In the last Home Challenge, you used your imaginations to think about how the aliens in MeeTu's world (or the executives at In-Touch Publishing) reacted to the scenes you sent them. What do you think their reactions were?

- What happened next in the story?

Discussion

1. Discuss how many interactions with others begin with someone initiating conversation. Point out that this can be scary, especially when you've tried to do this in the past and it hasn't worked out well, but that to have friends we must take risks.

2. Ask:

   - What are some ways we know that someone will be receptive to talking?

   - If they are not, how do we know?

   - What body language and facial expressions probably mean that someone wants to talk or doesn't want to talk?

   - If someone wants to talk with you and you don't want to talk, how do you let them know nicely?

3. Encourage participants to share a stories about a time they reached out to someone and started a conversation or a time they were afraid to do so. (Leaders may share their stories as well.)

Bus Stop

1. Place two chairs in one section of the room to represent the bench at a bus stop. Let participants know that the activity will involve taking turns sitting two at a time on the bench (or standing near the bench) waiting for a bus.

2. Begin the activity by having a group leader sit on the bench with a participant. Both pretend to be people waiting at a bus stop. The participant is challenged to initiate conversation with the group leader and to keep it going. A second challenge of the game is for the participant to accurately read nonverbal cues during small talk.

3. After the two have been talking for a minute or so, another group leader calls out that the bus has arrived. At that point, the group leader modeling the activity stands up and pretends to get on the bus, while the participant left at the bus stop moves over into the leader's seat. Another participant then takes a turn sitting at the bus stop, starting and continuing a conversation, and correctly reading nonverbal cues. One by one, each participant gets a chance to sit at the bus stop.

4. To make the game more interesting, you may choose to assign participants a specific character to play (or participants may pick a role out of a paper bag). Possible characters include:

   - Teenager into rock music

- Old man who is hard of hearing
- Businessman or woman late for an important meeting
- Little boy running away from home
- Teacher of a sixth-grade class
- Person with a very bad cold

Participants may also come up with their own characters.

Mad Scientist

1. In this activity, a group leader takes the role of "Dr. Literal." Explain the following context to participants:

   Dr. Literal has finally done it. After years of experimentation, with the help of his trusted lab assistant, Igor, he has successfully manipulated the human genome and created a human being from scratch! There is one slight problem. To cut some corners, Dr. Literal substituted a piece of plant DNA for a piece of the human genome. As a result, the creature takes everything that is said much too literally. The doctor discovered this when he had to take a bathroom break. Dr. Literal told the creature to wait a minute, and the creature waited exactly 60 seconds, no longer. Unfortunately, the creature got up before the doctor came back and tried to walk around the room without any feet, damaging himself in the process. Dr. Literal soon realized that he would have to teach the creature that some expressions have hidden meanings.

2. Tell participants that Dr. Literal needs their help to explain the following phrases to his creature:

   - Wait a minute.
   - Hold your horses.
   - I'll be there in a second.
   - I got your back.
   - I'm gonna kill you.
   - Eat your words.

3. Process the activity by discussing these expressions and any others that participants suggest.

The Worst Thing

1. Have the group sit in a circle. Begin this activity with a question: "What is the WORST thing that could happen if you try to start a conversation with someone?"

2. One participant thinks of the worst thing that could happen and what he or she would do in that situation. The next person takes that idea, thinks of the worst that could happen as a result, and so on. An example might go something like this:

Q: What is the worst thing that could happen if you went up and talked with someone who didn't want to talk to you?

A: They could say something mean to you.

Q: And then what would happen?

A: I would feel bad.

Q: And what's the worst thing that could happen then?

A: No one would ever be my friend, and everyone would hate me.

Q: What evidence do you have that this will happen?

3. Continue the activity until everyone has had a chance to contribute or as time permits.

> *One purpose of this activity is to allow participants to face some of their fears and come up with realistic solutions. Another purpose is to break down certain thoughts or negative predictions that might be unrealistic or get in the way of proactive social behaviors.*

Wrap-up

1. Discuss the session content. Questions to the group could include the following:
   - What did you learn today about starting conversations?
   - How can you use what we talked about today in your own life?
   - What did you learn from the Dr. Literal activity?

2. Give each participant a copy of the Home Challenge and answer any questions the group might have about the assignment. Remind them that they will have a chance to discuss their responses to the challenge at the beginning of the next session.

Session 13 Home Challenge

Try going up to someone and starting a conversation. Pick someone safe—someone you know will probably respond in a friendly way. Make sure to look at this person's nonverbal cues to see how they react. If you know the person well (for instance, if it's a family member) and you are not sure how they are feeling or reacting to you, check it out by asking them.

You can write about your experience, draw a picture, or discuss your thoughts with your parents.

Session 14

Dealing with Teasing

OBJECTIVES

- Discuss and normalize feelings and fears about being teased or left out.
- Reframe interpretations about why these situations might happen or have happened in the past and what they mean.
- Brainstorm ideas about what to do in these situations.
- Role-play these strategies through "tag" improvisations.

MATERIALS

Talking stick

Easel pad or poster board and marker

Assorted hats and other costume items for improvisations

Copies of the Home Challenge assignment

PROCEDURE

Warm-up

Conduct any of the following activities: Jello Room (Session 5), Slow-Motion Freeze Tag (Session 6), or Bubble Gum (Session 7).

Home Challenge Review

Encourage participants to share their responses to the Home Challenge. Discuss how the conversation experiments went. Make sure everyone who wants to has a chance to share a story about initiating a conversation. Discuss possible reasons why conversations were or were not successful. Praise all efforts at initiating conversation and encourage participants to keep practicing, just as they would keep practicing an instrument, a sport, a video game, or anything else they want to improve at.

Discussion

1. Begin the discussion by saying that everyone is left out sometimes and teased sometimes. Ask, "How does it feel when this happens?"

If you wish, as a group leader, share personal stories about times you had these experiences. This can really help participants feel understood and safe to express their own stories.

2. Discuss why some kids might be mean to other kids. If participants don't know or can't come up with any answer besides "They're mean," raise other possibilities (e.g., they are showing off, they are angry about something, they feel bad about themselves, they think that this will help them fit in).

3. Invite participants to brainstorm some things to do when they are left out or teased. Write all of their ideas on the easel pad or poster board. Possible strategies:

   • Get an adult.

   • Ignore the teaser (don't react or let them see that it bothers you).

   • Walk away.

   • Be assertive and firmly ask the person to stop.

   • Laugh at yourself.

   • Ask to be included if you are left out.

   • Try not to take it personally. (If someone doesn't want to play with you, why would you want to play with them?)

   • Ask someone else to play or join you in an activity.

   • Make a joke.

4. Ask participants to brainstorm some things they probably shouldn't do in these cases. For example:

   • Become violent.

   • Take it personally.

   • Start teasing other people.

   • Become visibly upset.

   Ask, "Why might these things not be such good ideas?"

5. Ask, "How can you know when someone is being mean when they are teasing you or if they are just teasing you in a friendly way?" Possible responses:

   • Ask what the person means.

   • Look at the nonverbal cues

   • Think of past situations with this person. Is there a trend in the way the person has behaved?

"Tag" Improvisations

1. Invite two participants to begin an improvisation dealing with being teased or left out. Suggested scenes:

   • You want to play with someone and they won't let you.

   • Your mom made you wear a sweater to school that your Great Aunt Matilda made. It is pink and has a bunny on it.

- Your mom drops you off at school and gives you a big juicy kiss in front of the other kids.
- You were the only one to get 100 on a test. The other kids tease you about it.
- You're playing soccer in gym, and the ball comes toward you. When you try to kick it, you miss and fall on your behind.
- You're in the hall at school and overhear two other kids talking about you.
- Someone doesn't like you, but you don't know why. When they pass you in the hall, they give you a big shove.
- Your teacher tells the class to get into groups for a social studies project. You walk over to two other kids and ask to be in their group. They walk away.

2. Continue the activity in the following way:

The two participants begin the scene. They may be replaced in two ways: They may be tagged by another group member, who gently touches their hand, or they may appeal to be tagged by putting a hand out, palm up, and waiting for another group member to tag them. Any member of the group can decide to tag or respond to a request to be tagged. The task is to keep the flow of the improvisation going. Through this activity, participants can explore a variety of ways to handle situations in which they are teased or left out.

If participants can't enact a scene with a positive, prosocial solution, ask them to redo it and help them come up with a better solution, using the previously discussed strategies. Discuss how one strategy works better than another.

It may be a good idea to set the guideline that at least half a minute should pass before someone tags or appeals to be tagged.

Wrap-up

1. Discuss session content:

- Everyone at some time or another has been teased or left out, and this doesn't feel very good. Which of the strategies we discussed do you think might help you the most?
- Sometimes kids tease other kids or leave them out because they think that they will be more popular that way. What are some better ways to be liked?

2. Give each participant a copy of the Home Challenge and answer any questions the group might have about the assignment. Remind them that they will have a chance to share their responses at the next session.

3. Tell the group that there are two sessions left in the program. Mention the last-session celebration at this point and give participants some advance notice about what it will involve (parent participation, food, etc.). Let them know that they will get more information about this at the next session.

Session 14 Home Challenge

If there is an opportunity, practice the strategies we talked about today for dealing with teasing and being left out.

You can write about your experience, draw a picture, or discuss your thoughts with your parents.

Session 15

Content Review

OBJECTIVES

- Review skills learned overall.
- Process feelings about ending the group.
- Express memorable moments with a partner in a creative, physical way.
- Make a group decision about what cooperative activity to share with parents on the last day.
- Make positive predictions for the future by creating "partner sculptures."

MATERIALS

Talking stick

Paper and markers

Copies of the Home Challenge and a note to parents, inviting them to attend the last session's wrap-up and party.

A sample note to parents appears on page 137. Please revise this note to fit the particulars of your situation.

PROCEDURE

Warm-up

Invite the group to nominate one of their favorite games for a warm-up activity. Take several nominations and then call for a vote. If conflict arises as a result of this vote, use this as a therapeutic opportunity and resolve the conflict within the group.

Home Challenge Review

Encourage participants to share their responses to the Home Challenge. Ask participants whether they had a chance to practice some of the strategies for dealing with teasing and discuss their experiences.

Discussion

Encourage participants to discuss their feelings about the group's ending soon. Emphasize past successes and important learning moments for each participant. These may not necessarily be related to session content but to relationships between participants. For example, a key learning moment for one of our participants was seeing a videorecording of himself and realizing that he looked really "hyper" and that this was difficult for others. Another participant had a key learning moment when he resolved a conflict with someone else, forgave him, and moved on. If participants have specific goals they are working on (e.g., not interrupting), group leaders might point out that they really showed improvement with this during a certain activity.

Partner Sculptures

Have participants pair up and, using their own bodies, create human sculptures or statues that illustrate certain moments they have experienced during the group process. These can be moments from favorite games or key interactions that helped them to learn concepts. Partners may wish to create a sculpture depicting a moment from a process drama or a funny moment that happened during the past weeks. For example:

- Two participants get into positions that look like the moment in the Standing in Someone Else's Shoes process drama when the talk show host is interviewing a guest.

- Two others might choose a moment from an active game like Slow-Motion Freeze Tag.

Group leaders should model this in advance so that participants understand what to do. This is similar to the Sculptors and Clay exercise in Session 5, but both participants work and move together so that their bodies represent the key experiences.

Dreams for the Future

1. Paraphrase the following:

   > Now that we are almost done with group, let's think about the future a little bit. What are some of your dreams for the future? Close your eyes and imagine 10 years from now. What would you like to be doing 10 or 15 years from now? Will you still be in school? What activities will you be involved in? What kinds of things will you be learning? What will you be good at? What career do you want to pursue?

2. Pass out paper and markers and ask participants to draw some of their dreams for the future. They may share them with others if they wish.

Preparation for the Last Session

1. Invite the group to choose a cooperative activity to teach the parents during the last session. Participants will have their own ideas, but parents in our groups

have had fun trying out Jello Room (Session 5), Birthday Gifts (Session 7), and Clones (Session 2), to name a few. (Your group may identify entirely different experiences.)

> *Problem-solve with the group: What would be a fun activity to share with the parents and why? What if parents don't want to play?*

2. Ask participants if they would like to explain the activity to the parents or whether they would like leaders to explain. If more than one participant would like to explain the activity, they can share this role.

Wrap-up

1. Briefly discuss session content and remind participants about the upcoming last session. Ask:

   - Did the activities today help you review things that we learned in the group?
   - Are there any important activities that you would have liked to do more than once?

2. Give each participant a copy of the Home Challenge and answer any questions the group might have about the assignment. Let the group know that they will have a chance to share their responses during the next session.

3. Give each participant the note to take home to parents reminding them about the last session's party.

Session 15 Home Challenge

We're nearing the end of our group. What has this experience been like for you? Is there anything that you thought or felt about it that was difficult to share with the group? If so, what was it? What do you want to remember about this group? What do you think you will take with you that you've learned?

You can write your responses, draw a picture, or discuss your thoughts with your parents.

Sample Note to Parents

Dear Parents:

Well, we've made it to the end of our group! It has been a very rewarding experience getting to know and work with your children. For our upcoming last session on _____, we would like to celebrate our group's successful completion. You are invited to be a part of it. Please be prepared to join your children in at least one activity. We will be providing some light snacks and drinks for refreshments. If your child is on a specific diet (for instance, allergic to nuts, dairy, gluten, or other foods), please let us know and/or bring a snack appropriate for him or her. We will do our best to provide healthy, nonallergenic snacks.

Thank you again for allowing your child to participate in our program. We look forward to seeing you next week!

Sincerely,
Group leaders

Session 16

Good-bye and Closure

OBJECTIVES

- Discuss the group experience.
- Give positive feedback to peers and receive positive feedback from peers.
- Engage in a cooperative activity with parents.
- Celebrate time spent together and say good-bye.

This last session and the prospect of saying good-bye may elicit a variety of feelings in participants and leaders. Don't be surprised if participants act out these feelings in various ways, including oppositional behaviors and regression to old habits. The presence of parents at this last session will also affect both participants and leaders. It is tempting for leaders to want to use this session as a way to please parents and show them how well the intervention "worked." The key here is to remember that the day is about the participants, not the parents—and definitely not about leaders or their agenda. Don't worry too much about whether the activity is being conducted correctly or the participants are performing as you wish they would. Celebrate the growth that the participants have made, whether or not they demonstrate it, and normalize any unexpected behavior that may arise.

MATERIALS

Paper, markers, and masking tape

Copies of the Award Certificate, final Home Challenge assignment, and Parent Evaluation Form

Healthy snacks for the party (if possible, dairy- and gluten-free items for participants on these diets)

Music CD and CD player

PROCEDURE

Warm-up

Either the participants or leaders invite and encourage parents to engage in the activity the group chose during the previous session. Participants are encouraged to explain the activity to their parents and teach them how to play.

Home Challenge Review

- Encourage participants to share their responses to the Home Challenge: Was the group experience what you expected? Why or why not?
- What will you remember and take with you?

    Processing thoughts and feelings related to this experience is an important skill in and of itself. Group leaders can model this by sharing their own thoughts and feelings about the experience.

Discussion

As a group, leaders and participants talk about saying good-bye and discuss what they have learned about themselves and one another. Leaders describe the growth they've seen in participants, talking about their feelings about the group's ending and asking participants to do the same. It is especially important for leaders to normalize feelings, both negative and positive, that might arise at the end of the program.

> *Taking enough time to say good-bye, and honoring the feelings that accompany the group's ending, is an important part of the intervention process.*

Compliments on the Back

> *While participants do the following activity, parents may fill out program evaluation forms.*

1. Have everyone pair up (leaders included) and have partners tape a sheet of paper to each other's backs. Let participants know that they will be going around the room and writing a nice thing about each person on the piece of paper taped to the person's back.

2. Emphasize that participants should write something nice for the person to remember them by. Explain that this is an opportunity to give positive feedback that might be difficult to say directly and also to have a written record of the friends they've made.

3. With another leader, model the process by writing something for each other. Provide suggestions if participants seem unsure of where to begin (e.g., "You have a nice laugh" or "You are a good friend").

    Leaders should monitor what participants are writing to make sure that all comments are appropriate. Each participant writes his or her name by the comment.

Awards Presentation

Give each participant an award for participating in and completing the group sessions. You can fill out a copy of the award on page 143 for each participant or take this opportunity to provide each participant with an award reflecting that participant's unique growth.

Personalized award certificates are easy to make with basic word-processing software. Awards may reflect progress on participants' individual goals, humorous references to fun moments in the previous weeks, or a combination of both. If you use the form on page 143, insert a specific trait on the blank line. Examples include friendship skills, social perception, cooperation, leadership, perseverance, courage, patience, ability to resolve conflicts, creative ideas, great sense of humor, and so forth.

Good-bye Party

Use the rest of the session for a good-bye party with food, drink, and music for parents, participants, and group leaders to enjoy together. Provide paper and pens for parents to exchange contact information if they wish.

In our experience, it is not uncommon for parents to want to keep in contact with one another so that their children can maintain friendships. Also, many parents have benefited from communicating regularly with, and gaining support from, other parents who share similar experiences in raising children with social difficulties.

Final Home Challenge

Here it is: the final challenge. Although group is over, many wonderful things are yet to come. Every day, think of ONE WAY that you can practice a skill you learned in group and do it.

- For example, maybe you can tell someone how you are feeling or ask them to tell you how they feel if you aren't sure.

- Or you can start a conversation with someone in your class or take the risk to join a group. You've proven that you can do it here.

Finally, as you leave group, remember us, and don't get discouraged if social situations aren't always easy. We are lucky to have gotten to know you in group. You can do it!

From *SCIP: Social Competence Intervention Program—A Drama-Based Intervention for Youth on the Autism Spectrum,* © 2008 by L. A. Guli, A. D. Wilkinson, and M. Semrud-Clikeman, Champaign, IL: Research Press (800-519-2707, www.researchpress.com)

Certificate of Achievement

By virtue of the authority vested in us by the Universitarus Theatricalus, we hereby bestow upon you

the award of Most Excellent Contribution to the Group Experience

as well as

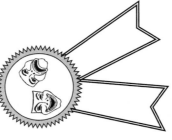

Awarded this _____ day in _____ of the year

Leader Signatures:

_____

_____

_____

Parent Evaluation Form

1. On a scale of 1–10, how would you rate your child's experience in the Social Competence Intervention Program (SCIP)?

2. Have you noticed any improvements in your child's social functioning? If so, what?

3. What was the most helpful aspect of the program?

4. What was the least helpful aspect of the program?

5. How do you think SCIP can be improved?

6. Would you recommend this program to other parents of children with similar difficulties?

7. Additional comments:

Appendix

Process Dramas

Suggestions for Conducting the Dramas

The following thoughts are intended to serve as a guide when conducting process dramas. Please remember that since the very nature of process drama is open ended, the sample dialogues we provide are *not* meant to be followed as scripts but are offered only to illustrate a possible direction as you improvise your own experiences.

As your dramas evolve, they will provide numerous and unpredictable teaching moments arising from the unique qualities and personalities of participants and group leaders. With this in mind, please feel free to add props and substitute your own creative ideas as they come. Or, if you have more leaders or adults present, add more characters to the dramas. Overall, be flexible. Participants will observe your ability to adapt to the changing needs of the group, time, and space and learn to be flexible and adapt in turn.

Finally, at all times, remember that it is the *process* that is central to the drama, rather than the product. In other words, if the drama does not enfold as you intended, use what *did* happen during the session to teach the session's objectives in the best way that you can. To illustrate some of the very different ways process dramas might unfold, three alternate scenarios following Process Drama 1 are provided to suggest three very different paths this detective story might take.

Process Drama 1

Detective Agency

Summary and Context

Money from the register and a valuable gaming system have been stolen from the Game Whiz gaming store. Participants have been called in as detectives to try to solve the crime. In doing so, they interview suspects and try out various strategies to interpret the intent behind nonverbal cues that do not match the suspects' verbal messages.

If one or more participants you are working with has an interest (e.g., video games, dinosaurs, biology, etc.), you may wish to incorporate this interest into your process drama to help engage them. The scene of the crime and specifics of the drama may change as long as the drama's objectives and general structure are followed. For example, if animals are a popular interest, a zoo or pet store could be the scene of the crime.

Roles

Group leaders play the following parts:

Chief Detective

Assistant Chief Detective

Suspect 1: Night-Shift Employee

Suspect 2: Store Manager

Participants play the part of detectives.

Suggested Evidence

Sample evidence pointing to the Store Manager as the guilty party includes the following:

Empty boxes to stolen goods, wires, and so forth (found in the Store Manager's car)

Smudged fingerprints from the scene

Muddy footprints

The code to the store's alarm system, written down on the back of a receipt

A letter from the Game Whiz company saying that the manager will not be receiving a bonus this year (see sample on page 155)

A blog written by the manager stating that the store "got what it deserved"

Other Props and Materials

Detective badges, crime scene tape, and assorted costumes (hats, ties, suit jackets, etc.)

Telephone *(optional—for a call from headquarters)*

Preparation

Set up one area of the room as the scene of the theft at the Game Whiz store and another area of the room as the Chief Detective's office.

Conducting the Drama

Before beginning the drama, briefly describe the situation. Give each participant a detective's badge and have participants choose costume items to reflect their roles. They can also choose detective names for themselves.

INTRODUCTION

The Chief Detective welcomes the other detectives into his or her office and explains that the detective agency has just been assigned a very important case. They have been chosen to work this case because of their exceptional ability to solve crimes, especially by interviewing suspects and determining who is telling the truth. Two suspects have been apprehended—the Store Manager, Sam Flakey, and the Night-Shift Employee, Mona Rock. The detectives will have a chance to question them both.

Chief Detective:

Thank you all for being here today. I called you in over the holiday because the agency has experienced a most unusual request. I'm sure all of you are familiar with the Game Whiz store at our main mall. It seems that last night the store was burglarized. The security system was dismantled and all of the cash taken from the cash register. Worse, the store was about to host the introduction of a new and expensive type of gaming system to the public this morning, but the system was stolen. We need your help in solving this crime PRONTO! So far, the store has narrowed down the suspects to two possible individuals: the Store Manager and the Night-Shift Employee. You will have a chance to interview these individuals after you examine the crime scene.

EXAMINING THE CRIME SCENE

Participants next visit the crime scene and examine the evidence. Allow participants to briefly walk about the room and look at the "evidence" placed by the group leaders. Because of the relatively unstructured nature of this activity, participants may become distracted at this point. To help them stay on task, give them specific instructions and parameters in which to explore the scene. For example, you may give participants one to two minutes to look for evidence and ask them to take notes about what they see.

INTERVIEWING THE FIRST SUSPECT

Chief Detective:

> Before I call in the first suspect, think carefully about the sort of questions that you will ask and how you might be able to tell if these suspects are telling the truth. Pay careful attention to their nonverbal cues, such as facial expression, tone of voice, and body language. I assure you, this is a very serious crime. We're all counting on you to solve it!

Ask participants:

- What sort of questions will you ask the suspects?
- How might you be able to tell if the suspects are telling the truth?

The Night-Shift Employee is the first suspect to be questioned. The employee is innocent and conveys sincerity in body language, facial expression, and vocal tone. Some suggestions include using a calm voice, making eye contact with the questioner, and keeping the body still and relaxed. Facial and vocal expression should match the words as well as each other. For example, the employee should not smile nervously when being questioned about serious matters and should not overemphasize her innocence.

Night-Shift Employee:

> Well, last night, I was leaving early, which was unusual. There was this great band in town, and I wanted to hear them play. So I gave the keys to the Store Manager and asked him to close up the shop for me. He said it was no problem. Before I left, I counted the money in the register and looked over the merchandise. Oh, and I made sure everything was in place for the big demonstration the next day. Nothing seemed unusual. The manager said he would set up the security system. This morning I was told there was a break-in.

The detectives next ask any questions they want. If they ask questions regarding the evidence, the Night-Shift Employee can, of course, answer these, but the Chief Detective or other leaders should redirect participants' attention to the suspect by asking questions about the suspect's nonverbal cues.

When the detectives have finished their questioning, the employee is excused, and the Chief Detective encourages them to discuss the interview.

Chief Detective:

> All right, everyone, settle down, now we need to get to work. I hope you were all paying very close attention to the suspect's explanation—not just the suspect's words but the suspect's facial expressions, tone of voice, and body language. I'd like to hear what each of you

thinks about the Night-Shift Employee's guilt or innocence. I'm going to ask several questions, and we can discuss each in turn.

Ask participants:

- Did the Night-Shift Employee seem to be telling the truth or lying?
- Did the suspect's gestures and facial expressions match her words?
- Did the suspect's tone of voice match her words?
- How do you think the suspect was feeling?

INTERVIEWING THE SECOND SUSPECT

The Store Manager, Sam Flakey, next enters for questioning. The suspect is guilty and therefore should appear to be lying by sending contradictory cues through tone of voice, body language, and facial expression. For example, the manager might proclaim innocence in an anxious or angry tone of voice, smile at the same time, answer questions without making eye contact or with eyes darting back and forth, hunch shoulders, or indicate nervousness by tapping his foot.

Again, the detectives may ask any questions they wish. The manager may answer questions about the evidence, but the Chief Detective or other leaders should bring participants' attention back to the suspect's nonverbal cues and the mismatch between those cues and the suspect's statements.

When the detectives have finished their questioning, the Store Manager is excused, and the Chief Detective leads discussion of the interview.

Ask participants:

- Did the Store Manager seem to be telling the truth or lying?
- Did the suspect's gestures and facial expressions match his words?
- Did the suspect's tone of voice match his words?
- How do you think the suspect was feeling?
- How did this interview compare with the previous interview?

PRESENTATION OF ADDITIONAL EVIDENCE

If participants are having difficulty with questions or are off task, the Chief Detective may decide to receive an "unexpected phone call" to introduce new and helpful evidence or information, found either at the crime scene or in the Store Manager's home or car. This evidence can be presented at any time deemed appropriate by the group leaders and brought in for the detectives to examine. Evidence that could be withheld until this point might include a part of a blog or e-mail written by the Store Manager about the store's "getting what it deserved" or the code for the store's alarm, written on a receipt found with the Store Manager's things. The detectives should be encouraged to question the suspects about the evidence. Evidence should be exciting enough to continue engaging participants' interest in the drama, but group leaders should emphasize that the true answers to the crime lie in the interviews with suspects.

Receiving the unexpected phone call from headquarters is an opportunity for group leaders to get the group's attention or help the drama progress if necessary.

CONCLUSION

After all of the evidence has been reviewed and the suspects have been interviewed to the detectives' satisfaction, the Chief Detective encourages the detectives to discuss the case and determine what they think happened. Once they have decided who perpetrated the crime, the chief leads the Store Manager in and performs an arrest. At this point, the suspect confesses to the crime.

The Store Manager confirms guilt even if the group participants have taken the drama in an unexpected direction and developed an alternate theory. Although the plot is always open for development by participants, it is intended that the solution to the crime depend on the decoding of nonverbal cues and awareness of mismatched cues.

Alternate Scenarios

Process dramas don't always go as planned, and this one is no exception. For example, participants may decide that the store was robbed by more than one person, or a creative, attention-seeking group member might shout, "IT'S ME! I DID IT! I ADMIT IT!" in the middle of the drama. If this happens, group leaders will need to think on their feet. They can handle unexpected plot turns in any way that still allows for the drama's objectives to be met. For example, the Chief Detective could steer the drama so that it appears that the participant who blurted out the admission of guilt was trying to protect his friend, the Store Manager, or the chief could reframe this sudden admission of guilt as a joke.

To illustrate the flexible, unscripted nature of process drama, here are three additional possible scenarios showing how the detective drama might evolve.

SCENARIO 1

Participants explore the scene and interview both suspects. As hoped, detectives infer that the Store Manager is lying, based on this suspect's nonverbal cues. Their suspicion is confirmed by the presentation of additional evidence and a confession by the manager. Suddenly, one of the detectives confesses and says that he was also working with the Store Manager. The group leaders work with this plot twist, and the detective is arrested and led away with the Store Manager.

SCENARIO 2

Participants explore the scene and interview both suspects. One participant suspects that the Night-Shift Employee is guilty, based on some evidence found on the scene. This participant adds to the story, saying that he saw this employee, in fact, the night before, when the participant was walking by the store, and the employee was carrying out a large box to his car! Now that this eyewitness testimony is also part of the story, the Assistant Chief works with this information and calls the store employee back for more questioning. When asked about taking a box out of the store, the employee admits, conveying sincerity, that he was taking this box home because he was collecting moving boxes. The Assistant Chief points out the fact that the employee appears very sincere due to his nonverbal cues and then introduces further evidence to implicate the Store Manager.

SCENARIO 3

Participants explore the scene. As they explore, two participants begin arguing, and one of them leaves the room upset. The other goes to a corner of the room, where he huddles in a ball. One group leader leaves the room to bring back the participant who left, while another works with the student in the corner. Since questioning of suspects can't begin because the two group leaders playing these roles are working individually with students, the Assistant Chief calls over the detectives for a quick meeting. In role, the Assistant Chief explains that sometimes conflict happens among detectives but that part of working together as a strong team is learning to resolve those conflicts and move past them. Suddenly, the door opens, and the angry participant enters with the group leader behind him. He says, "This is all fake—I'm not doing any of it," and sits down near the door. The Assistant Chief asks everyone to sit down, and the group processes the conflict together, including in the discussion some information about how nonverbal cues played a role in expressing emotion. After this, since there is no time in the session for extended interviewing of suspects, the suspects briefly present their cases for innocence. During the interview of the Store Manager, the Assistant Chief asks the detectives if they notice anything strange about the Store Manager's way of communicating. The Store Manager confesses his guilt.

> As you can see, group leaders need to be able to think on their feet to improvise so as to accommodate any unexpected plot twists introduced by the detectives. Almost anything should be allowed to become a part of the plot (even if an imaginary fire breaks out in the police station). This ability to think flexibly is in and of itself an important skill for the group participants to develop. However, at the same time, group leaders should do their best to focus the detectives on the objective: decoding nonverbal cues.

Sample Letter to Store Manager

Dear Mr. Flakey:

This letter is to inform you that you will unfortunately not be receiving the holiday bonus this year usually received by all store managers. Due to unseen budget cutbacks, we have been forced to reexamine our resources and have decided to limit our bonuses to the few people who have shown outstanding performance. We hope you try harder and help make this next year a better one for our company!

Sincerely,
Game Whiz Management

Excerpt from Blog or E-mail Found on Work Computer

I can't believe they did this! This week has really been awful. I really hate working at this store! They're gonna pay, though. They're gonna get what they deserve.

Process Drama 2

Edna Snipes

Summary and Context

The Prime Minister's birthday cake is missing from the kitchen. Participants, assuming the role of detectives, are called in by Scotland Yard to help solve the crime. They must piece together facts from clues and, most important, interview witnesses and decide whom to believe based on whether the suspects' nonverbal cues match each other as well as their verbal messages.

Roles

Group leaders play the following parts:

Assistant Chief of Scotland Yard

Suspect 1: Kitchen Manager

Suspect 2: Ms. Edna Snipes (Assistant to the Prime Minister)

Participants assume the roles of Scotland Yard detectives.

Suggested Evidence

An empty plate

Birthday candles and a fork with chocolate frosting on them

A file folder containing a not-so-good midyear job evaluation for Ms. Snipes

A purse containing an Overeaters Anonymous Card, a napkin with chocolate frosting on it, and a number of empty candy wrappers

A blank (or partially filled-in) job application

> *The Overeaters Anonymous Card, Edna's job evaluation, and a generic job application appear on pages 162–163. If you wish, you could gather a few more job applications from fast-food or retail stores.*

Other Props and Materials

Miscellaneous kitchen items (bowls, spoons, measuring cups, etc.)

Detective badges, crime scene tape, and assorted costumes (hats, ties, suit jackets, etc.)

Telephone (*optional—for a call from headquarters*)

Preparation

Set up one area of the room as the crime scene (the Prime Minister's kitchen), including the evidence and other kitchen items. Set up another area as a location at Scotland Yard for interviewing the suspects.

Conducting the Drama

Before beginning, briefly describe the situation. Give each participant a detective's badge and invite them to choose costume items to reflect their role. They could also choose detective names for themselves.

INTRODUCTION

The Assistant Chief welcomes the detectives into the conference area and explains that the Chief of Scotland Yard has just assigned them a very important case to solve. They have been especially chosen to work this case because of their exceptional ability to solve crimes by interviewing suspects. Two suspects have been apprehended: the Kitchen Manager and Ms. Edna Snipes. The detectives will have a chance to question them both.

Assistant Chief:

> Good day to you all. You've been called in to solve a most troubling crime. I am here to report that at 8:00 P.M., the Prime Minister's birthday cake was found to be missing. Stolen. It was quietly taken during the Prime Minister's birthday party, directly from the kitchen. There were no witnesses. However, after initial investigation, two suspects have been apprehended, the Prime Minister's Assistant, a Ms. Edna Snipes, and the Kitchen Manager. You detectives will have a chance to question both of them after you examine the crime scene.

EXAMINING THE CRIME SCENE

Participants next visit the crime scene and examine the evidence. Allow participants to walk about the room briefly and look at the items placed by the group leaders. Because of the relatively unstructured nature of this activity, participants may become distracted. To help them stay on task, give them specific instructions and parameters with which to explore the scene. For example, you might give participants one to two minutes to look for evidence and ask them to take notes about what they see.

INTERVIEWING THE FIRST SUSPECT

After they have examined the crime scene, the detectives return to the conference area.

Assistant Chief:

> You will now have the chance to interview the two suspects in this crime. I assure you, this is a most serious matter. The Prime Minister

has been known to call a state of national emergency in response to missing cake. We're all counting on you. You will be able to ask the suspects anything you want, and it will be up to you to pay careful attention to their nonverbal cues—facial expression, voice, and body language—in order to determine whether they are telling the truth. The first suspect is the Kitchen Manager.

Ask participants:

- What sort of questions will you ask the suspects?
- How might you be able to tell if the suspects are telling the truth?

The Kitchen Manager enters for questioning. The manager is innocent and should therefore convey sincerity in body language, facial expression, and tone—specifically, by using a calm voice, making eye contact with the questioner, and keeping the body still and relaxed. Facial and vocal expression should match the words as well as each other. For example, the employee should not smile nervously when being questioned about serious matters and should not overemphasize his innocence.

Kitchen Manager:

> Well, last night was no different from usual. I finished preparing the menu for the next day and was putting the finishing touches on the cake for the Prime Minister's birthday celebration. It was a beautiful chocolate cake—thick, buttercream frosting, banana filling, and chocolate shavings. One of my best . . . mmm . . . anyway, as I was saying. I cleaned up my supplies, made sure all the appliances were turned off, and went home. I locked the door before I left as I usually do. This morning, I received a call from the police saying there was a break-in. I have no idea how or why it happened. Of course, I know my cakes are good, but no one's ever STOLEN one before!

At this point, the detectives may ask any questions they wish. When the detectives have finished their questioning, the Kitchen Manager is excused, and the Assistant Chief asks the detectives to discuss the interview.

Assistant Chief:

> All right, everyone, settle down, now we need to get to work. I hope you were all paying very close attention to the suspect's answers and explanations—not just the suspect's words, but the facial expressions, tone of voice, and body language. I'd like to hear what each of you thinks about the Kitchen Manager. I'm going to ask several questions, and we can discuss each in turn.

- First, did the Kitchen Manager seem to be telling the truth or lying?
- Did the Kitchen Manager's gestures and expressions match his words?
- Did the tone of voice match the words?
- How do you think the Kitchen Manager was feeling?

INTERVIEWING THE SECOND SUSPECT

Ms. Edna Snipes enters for questioning. She is guilty and so should appear to be lying by sending contradictory cues through tone of voice, body language, and facial expression. For example, Edna might proclaim innocence in an anxious or angry tone of voice, smile at the same time, answer questions without making eye contact or with eyes darting back and forth, hunch her shoulders, or indicate nervousness by tapping her foot.

Edna Snipes:

> Um . . . you wanted to see me? I know nothing about this, you know.
> Absolutely nothing! I don't know why I'm being questioned. I don't
> even like cake! Umm . . . cake. In fact, I'm on a very carefully
> controlled diet. Working near the kitchen has been . . . particularly
> hard for me. I have worked loyally in the Prime Minister's residence
> for over 20 years! I would never do something like steal his cake! I
> love my job. I really do. It makes me very happy.

Again, the detectives can ask Ms. Snipes any questions they wish. When the detectives have finished their questioning, Ms. Snipes is excused, and the Assistant Chief leads discussion of the interview.

Ask participants:

- Did Edna Snipes seem to be telling the truth or lying?
- Did her gestures and expressions match her words?
- Did her tone of voice match her words?
- How do you think Edna Snipes was feeling?
- How did this interview compare with the previous interview?

> *Try to steer the questions and discussion away from the evidence and toward*
> *the objective of decoding nonverbal cues.*

PRESENTATION OF ADDITIONAL EVIDENCE

At any time, the Assistant Chief may receive an unexpected phone call from headquarters, stating that additional evidence has been found at another location. This evidence can be brought in for the detectives to examine. The detectives should be encouraged to question the suspects about the evidence. Evidence should be exciting enough to continue engaging participants' interest in the drama, but group leaders should emphasize that the true answers to the crime lie in the interviews with the suspects.

> *Receiving an unexpected phone call is an opportunity to get participants'*
> *attention or help the drama progress if necessary. It is especially helpful if*
> *participants are having difficulty with questions or are off task.*

CONCLUSION

After all of the evidence has been reviewed and the suspects have been interviewed to the detectives' satisfaction, the Assistant Chief should encourage the detectives to discuss the case and determine what they think happened. Once they have decided who perpetrated the crime, the Assistant Chief can lead the suspect in and perform an arrest. At that point, Ms. Edna Snipes confesses to the crime. Edna Snipes confirms guilt even if the group participants take the drama in an unexpected direction, so that her guilt is consistent with the expression of mismatched nonverbal cues. Although the plot is always open for development by participants, it is intended that the true solution to the crime lie in the decoding of nonverbal cues.

The drama doesn't always go as planned, however. For example, participants may decide that the cake was stolen by more than one person, or a creative, attention-seeking group member might shout, "IT'S ME! I DID IT! I ADMIT IT!" in the middle of the drama. If this happens, group leaders can think on their feet and handle unexpected plot turns in any way that still allows for the drama's objectives to be met. For example, the Assistant Chief can steer the drama so that it appears that this participant was trying to protect his friend, the Kitchen Manager, or the cake theft could have been a team job, or the Assistant Chief can reframe this sudden admission of guilt as a joke.

```
┌─────────────────────────────────────────────┐
│                                             │
│            Overeaters Anonymous             │
│               Edna Snipes                   │
│           Member in Good Standing           │
│                                             │
│                                             │
└─────────────────────────────────────────────┘
```

Mid-Year Job Evaluation

Name: Ms. Edna Snipes   **Position:** Assistant to the Prime Minister

Comments:

Although Ms. Snipes has been working for the Prime Minister's Office for some time, her behavior recently has been of great concern. She has been late on more than one occasion, and her usual attention to detail has been lacking. Chocolate smudges have been left on more than one official memo. In addition, Ms. Snipes' attitude has gone downhill.

Recommendations:

Ms. Snipes is strongly encouraged to take advantage of our excellent employee counseling program to address the lapses in her performance. If her performance does not improve, dismissal should be considered an option.

Job Application

Name: _____

Address: _____

Phone number (home): _____ (cell): _____

E-mail: _____

Reason for seeking employment: _____

Previous work experience:

_____

_____

_____

Education:

_____

_____

_____

References:

_____

_____

_____

Why do you want to work for our organization?

_____

_____

_____

From *SCIP: Social Competence Intervention Program—A Drama-Based Intervention for Youth on the Autism Spectrum,* © 2008 by L. A. Guli, A. D. Wilkinson, and M. Semrud-Clikeman, Champaign, IL: Research Press (800-519-2707, www.researchpress.com)

Process Drama 3

Standing in Someone Else's Shoes

Summary and Context

In this drama, a group leader takes on the role of hosting a television talk show called "Standing in Someone Else's Shoes." Each week, the host invites guests with widely different opinions on specific topics and asks them to discuss why they believe what they do. Participants chosen as guests must understand and represent the point of view of the character they are assigned to play. At some point during the game show, a group leader rings a bell or sounds a noisemaker, at which point guests must switch seats, switch roles, and argue from the *other* point of view! Participants not chosen as guests become audience members who will observe the guests' interactions and be asked to comment on how well the guests represented their points of view. However, all participants should have an opportunity to be a talk show guest if time permits.

Roles

Group leaders play the following parts:

   Talk Show Host (Flashy Grins or Suzie Smiles)

   Callers *(optional)*

Participants take on the roles of talk show guests and audience.

Props and Other Materials

   Slips of paper, pencil, and a bag or hat

   Microphone (toy or real)

   Bell or other noisemaker

   Poster board and marker

   Desk and chairs

   Hat and jacket for host, other costume items for guests and audience members to choose from (hats, jackets, ties, etc.)

   Telephone *(optional)*

   CD player for theme music *(optional)*

Preparation

Write "The Standing in Someone Else's Shoes Show" on the poster board and display the sign prominently. Place two or three chairs in a row on one side of the room, forming an impromptu stage. Position a desk and chair slightly to the side for the talk show host, and place the microphone and telephone (if you wish) on the desk. Set up rows of chairs for the remaining participants to sit in, as audience members. Write the talk show topic and roles for the show's guests on slips of paper and place them in a hat or bag for participants to draw.

Conducting the Drama

One leader can play theme music on the CD player to help establish the context, if desired, just before the introduction.

INTRODUCTION

Host:

Welcome to the talk show that REALLY knows how you feel. Or at least we think we do! Now, we're not going to really take off our shoes and switch them (that might get very stinky). We're just using the expression "standing in someone else's shoes" to explain that we are going to try and see from each others' point of view. It's like we're going to pretend that we ARE them and try to guess what it is like to BE them. Our guests today will be giving their opinions on various topics and trying to convince us that they are right. But if they hear this sound *(ring bell or make noise with noisemaker),* they have to switch points of view!

SAMPLE QUESTION-ANSWER SEGMENT

One leader takes the role of host, while another leader plays the part of the guest. Leaders model a brief question-answer segment to give participants an idea of what the host and guest roles entail.

You might pretend the guest is a celebrity or famous politician or perhaps the school's principal—someone participants will know—and ask questions accordingly. For example, leaders might model with something like the following.

Host: Principal Miller, thank you for being here. Today we're going to talk about school lunches. Many people have strong opinions about them. I know I did when I was in school! Lately, some parents want to get rid of the cafeteria because they think that cafeteria food is not healthy. What is your opinion?

Principal: Thanks, Flashy. Well, I can see why parents are worried, but I think closing down the cafeteria would be a bad idea. Our cafeteria provides lots of healthy choices. We have salads, fruit, and lots of protein.

Host: But do kids ever choose the healthy foods?

Principal: Sure they do! And think about it: If we closed down the cafeteria, some kids who aren't able to bring lunch wouldn't get to eat lunch at all.

Host: Let's see what our other guest thinks. Welcome to our show, Mrs. Quigdonald. You have a son in Principal Miller's school. Tell us, what do you think about the cafeteria?

Parent: Well, last week, when I asked my son what he had for lunch, he said a bag of chips, a soda, and four chocolate cookies. That doesn't sound very healthy to me . . . so I think the cafeteria needs to be closed.

(Questions and answers continue.)

CHOOSING TALK SHOW TOPICS AND GUESTS

Leaders let participants know the topic for the talk show, chosen in advance, and draw roles for that topic from the hat or bag. (Alternatively, participants may suggest a topic.) The show's guests then select and dress in costume pieces appropriate for their roles. These may simply consist of hats and/or jackets. They may choose their own guest names, if they wish. Ideally, all participants should have the chance to be guests and to switch perspectives on the same topic as guests. If time doesn't allow for this, you may choose to limit the guests to certain participants by randomly picking their names from a hat or extend the drama to the following session, eliminating some activities from a future session if you think that extending this activity would be more valuable.

Sample topics and guests:

- Topic 1: A Colony on the Moon?

  Guest 1: For

  Guest 2: Against

- Topic 2: Cell Phones in Classrooms

  Guest 1: Teacher (against)

  Guest 2: Student (for)

- Topic 3: Let's Bring Dinosaurs Back to Life

  Guest 1: Scientist (wants to bring dinosaurs back to life)

  Guest 2: Environmentalist (thinks dinosaurs will hurt the Earth's existing habitats)

- Topic 4: Peanuts: Should We Stop Growing Them?

  Guest 1: Hates peanuts and is allergic to them

  Guest 2: Peanut farmer

PUTTING ON THE SHOW

The host and guests take their positions on the "stage." Almost anything can happen next. For example, if the topic "Peanuts: Should We Stop Growing Them?" is chosen by the group, the drama might progress as follows.

Host: Today's topic is peanuts! Should they be banned? Let's hear from today's guests. First, we have Guest 1, John Doe. Hi, John.

Guest 1: Hi.

Host: What do you think about peanuts?

Guest 1: Um . . . I hate them. They're awful. And I'm allergic to them.

Host: OK, you hate them. What do you think should be done?

Guest 1: Let's get rid of peanuts. Stupid food.

Host: Tell us more.

Guest 1: Um . . . *(Shrugs.)*

Host: *(Trying to help out participant)* If we got rid of them, how would that help you?

Guest 1: I could die if I eat them. I would be safer since I wouldn't have to be around them anymore. I think lots of kids are allergic to them.

Host: Yes, that's true. But I'm not sure everyone agrees with your idea to get rid of them. Let's see what our second guest has to say. Farmer Jones?

Guest 2: Yeah, that's me.

Host: I hear your main crop is peanuts. What do you think about getting rid of peanuts once and for all?

Guest 2: I think that would be a really bad idea. Growing peanuts is how I make money.

Host: *(To Guest 1)* What do you think about that?

Guest 1: Well, he could grow something else, like corn.

Guest 2: *(Turning to Guest 1)* You're stupid! Don't you . . .

At this point, group leaders may say, "Stop" or freeze the drama and remind the participant that name calling is not an OK way to respond. Group leaders ask the participant to come up with a different response. They may ask other participants, "Why is calling him stupid not a good idea?" Possible answers include "It would make him feel bad," "It isn't a good argument for peanuts," "It would cause more conflict," and so forth.

Guest 2: I don't want to grow anything else. There are people who like peanuts. Peanut butter is really popular. Just because he doesn't like it doesn't mean that no one should grow peanuts. My whole family loves them.

A group leader rings a bell, signaling that guests should switch seats and positions.

Host: Ah! There's our signal to *stand in someone else's shoes!* Guests, it's time for you to switch seats and see if you can argue from the other person's point of view. Now switch seats, switch roles, and continue debating this topic, but from the other person's perspective.

If participants look confused, the host clarifies what to do and leaders model it if necessary.

Host: John Doe *(or participant name)*, you are now Farmer Jones. Farmer Jones *(or participant name)*, you are now John Doe. Farmer Jones, what can you say about peanuts? As Farmer Jones, do you want to get rid of peanuts or keep farming them?

Guest 1: *(Now the peanut farmer)* I want to keep farming them?

Host: Great! Why?

Guest 1: Because . . . I make a lot of money doing that, and lots of people like peanut butter. Not everyone is allergic to it. Some people love it.

Host: And, John Doe, what do you have to say to that?

Guest 2: *(Now John Doe)* It doesn't matter if people love peanuts. If I'm near peanuts, I get really sick. And lots of other kids are allergic to them, too.

Host: What else?

If no one says anything, the host may decide to take a question from the audience, or another group leader may say that someone is calling in with a question.

CALLER AND AUDIENCE QUESTIONS

Calls from viewers and audience questions can serve several purposes. A group leader might choose to insert a call from a viewer as a way to steer the drama back on track, much as the unexpected phone call functions in the detective dramas. For example, if two guests begin to debate something unrelated to the talk show topic, a call from a viewer can bring the show back on topic. Also, if guests are having trouble defending their position and don't know what to say, audience questions or calls from viewers can help provide them with ideas. Finally, audience questions allow all group members to be actively engaged in the drama.

Continuing the previous process drama example, an audience question might function like this.

Host: Do we have any questions from the audience? *(Two audience members raise their hands. Another group leader calls on one of them and stands next to him or her with the microphone. The audience member takes the microphone.)*

Audience Member: Can't you just stay away from peanuts?

Host: Was that question for John Doe?

Audience Member: Yes.

Host: How do you want to answer that, John?

The participant who is playing John Doe answers, and the drama continues.

PROCESSING THE TALK SHOW DRAMA

After a topic has been discussed sufficiently and the show is over, leaders invite the audience members and guests themselves to comment on how well guests supported their opinions. Guests can also provide feedback to the audience about how well they paid attention. Sample questions might include these:

- Were the guests convincing in their roles? What about when they switched parts?
- If you were a guest, was it hard to switch parts and start arguing from the opposite point of view?
- Did you find your own opinions changing more as you heard more information?

> *If time permits, conduct another show on another topic. Give as many participants as possible a chance to take on a guest role.*

Process Drama 4

Space Mission

Summary and Context

It is the year 2273. A Space Station Commander announces to other astronauts aboard the station that an urgent message has arrived from the Intergalactic Conference. An unknown alien civilization is threatening to destroy the Earth because they are confused by the nonverbal component of human social interactions. The conference has chosen the astronauts on this station for an important mission because of their expertise in human social interactions. An alien ambassador is on the way, with whom the astronauts will be able to discuss the puzzling nature of communication in Earthlings' interactions. To keep the aliens from destroying the planet, the astronauts will also need to create a video message to send back to the alien world to show how nonverbal communication plays a part in typical situations on Earth.

Roles

Group leaders play the following parts:

Space Station Commander

MeeTu (the alien)

Participants play the part of astronauts aboard the space station.

Props and Other Materials

Costume items for Space Station Commander and astronauts

Props to create the space station environment

Preparation

Some creativity will come in handy on the part of the group leaders since they will need to costume the astronauts and suggest that the room is a space station. The props need not be expensive. For one group, the alien costume consisted of trash bags and an old belt. To create a sense of the space station, group leaders could use aluminum foil–covered boxes to simulate control panels and create large data screens or space station windows from poster board. The goal is not to create an elaborate set but simply to add some props to help engage participants in the scene. The space station itself exists in the minds of participants and leaders.

Part 1: Conducting the Drama

Explain that participants are astronauts aboard a space station and encourage them to choose and put on costume items to reflect this.

INTRODUCTION

Space Station Commander:

Welcome, astronauts. Our space station has received an urgent transmission from the Intergalactic Conference. It seems that an alien civilization at the edge of the galaxy has been picking up television signals from old sitcoms, but they do not understand them. Humans seem contradictory and dangerous to these aliens because they do strange things with their faces and bodies, and sometimes their voices sound different. The aliens have decided that we are a threat and that they must destroy all traces of humanity. The Intergalactic Conference has confidence in our space station's ability to save our planet, but to do so, we must explain these strange aspects of human communication in a way the aliens will understand. The alien civilization has agreed to give humans a chance to do this. They are sending their ambassador, MeeTu, to our space station. MeeTu is friendly to humans, has learned English for this mission, and wants to help the other aliens understand us. We will be able to talk to MeeTu and find out more about the alien world and what is confusing to them about us humans.

The Space Station Commander then helps the astronauts think of questions they would like to ask the alien. For example:

- How do you communicate on your planet?
- How can we help you?
- Why are we confusing to you?

INTERVIEWING MEETU

The alien MeeTu enters to talk with the astronauts. MeeTu does not understand or use any nonverbal social cues and should speak in a monotone with a flat facial expression.

MeeTu:

I am happy to be here. I am excited to learn about your civilization. It is very different from ours. We have been watching your world for a while, and we do not understand these things you do with your faces, bodies, and voices. On our world, we only use words. I want to help you. If you can teach us about these things you do, then I think our government will choose not to destroy your planet.

The astronauts next ask MeeTu their questions about the alien civilization.

Some participants may become fixated upon asking MeeTu questions about the alien civilization. This should be permitted; however, the majority of questions should involve social relationships and interactions. Otherwise, MeeTu or the Space Station Commander should steer participants back on topic.

MeeTu may also ask questions of the astronauts. These can be as general or as detailed as the participants can handle about how nonverbal cues work. For example:

- We know that the human mouth is used to help feed the body, but sometimes it goes up or down at the corners when we have not observed any food nearby. What does this mean?
- When the voice gets louder, does this signal that the human is going to attack?
- Why does the face move around so much when humans are communicating?
- We have picked up the word *emotion* from some of your radio transmissions. Can you explain?
- We have observed that the molecular compound H_2O sometimes comes out of the eyes. Why does the human leak? And when the human leaks, why does the face become red and squeezed? Usually the mouth goes down, but sometimes it goes up when the human leaks. Help us understand!

An unexpected message from the Intergalactic Conference to the Space Station Commander or from the alien world to MeeTu can be helpful in managing off-task behavior or assisting group progress. You can have a written message from the alien world be delivered (see page 174) or receive a message via futuristic communication devices (walkie-talkies work well).

Part 2: Recording and Reviewing the Interactions

Once MeeTu has allowed the participants to explain about nonverbal cues, the alien suggests that the astronauts create a videorecording to show how nonverbal communication works in various interactions on Earth. Participants will watch the recordings and have the opportunity to see themselves on the recording before giving them to MeeTu. MeeTu will take this recording back to the other aliens to show that the nonverbal parts of human communication can be understood and that humans mean them no harm.

To conclude the drama, MeeTu can give a final message. For example:

Thank you, humans. I am beginning to understand your strange ways. I will do my best to explain them to my people, and we will study the recordings you make. Perhaps we will not choose to destroy you after all.

Specific instructions for continuing the process drama are given in Session 12.

A Message from the Alien World

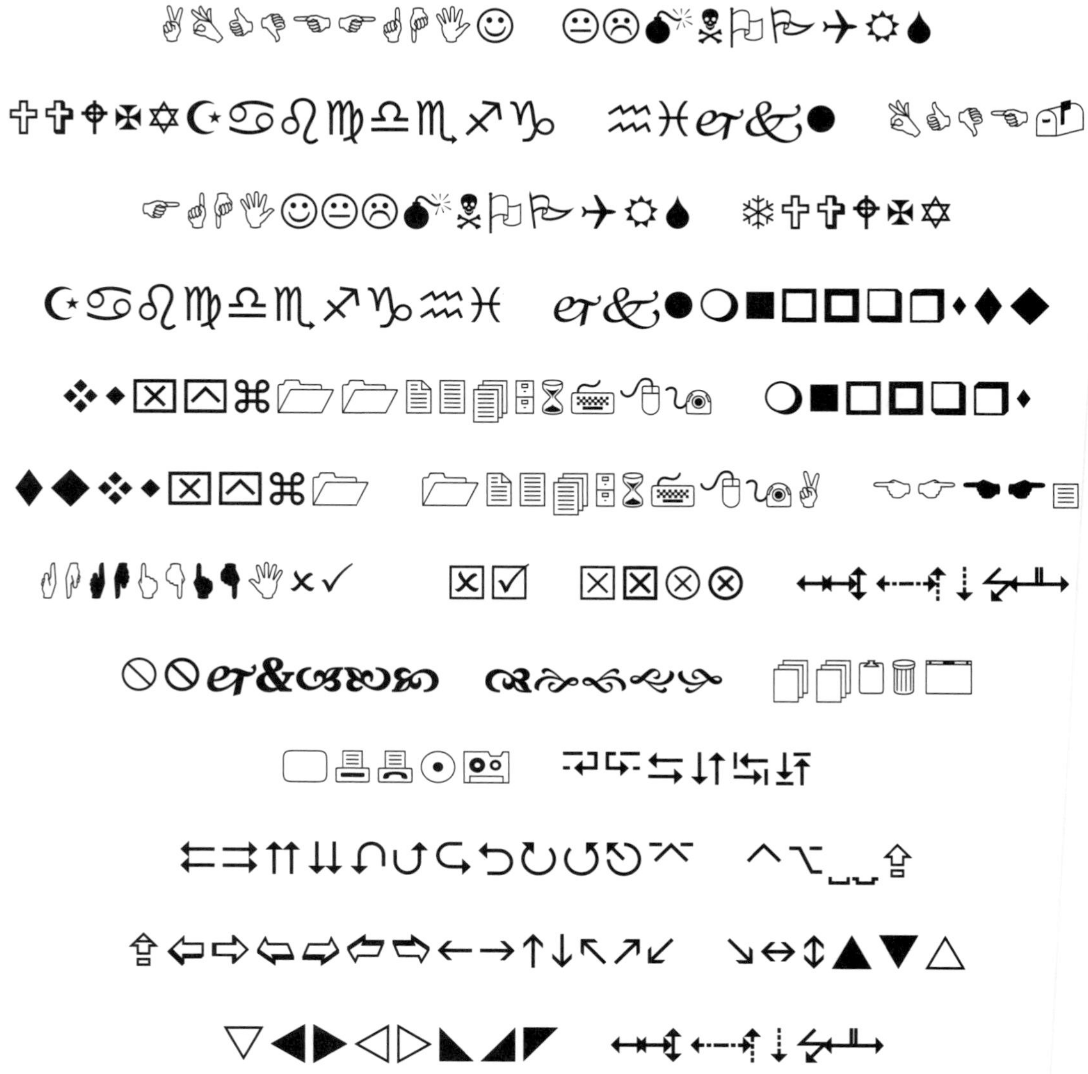

Process Drama 5

Advertising Agency

Summary and Context

In this drama, an advertising agency has received a request from a new client who needs help understanding what young people are like so that they can launch a new magazine. The client has asked that the agency prepare some videos of common social situations to help them understand what young people are like and how they communicate, both verbally and nonverbally. As advertising executives attempting to enlighten their client, participants will develop video vignettes of themselves acting out typical interactions that young people have.

Roles

Group leaders play the role of vice presidents of the advertising agency.

Participants play the role of agency executives.

Props and Other Materials

Costume items for the advertising executives (wigs, hats, jewelry, clip-on ties, etc.)

Poster board and markers

Copies of the letter from the Marketing Manager of In-Touch Publishing, Inc. *(optional)*

Preparation

A sign on the wall with the name of the ad agency can help set the atmosphere. Help the participants come up with a fun name for their agency and encourage them to adopt character roles for themselves.

Part 1: Conducting the Drama

INTRODUCTION

Vice President:

Good afternoon, everyone! I've called you all together because we have a contract for a new client. Our new client, Mr. M. Pathee from the In-Touch Publishing Agency, has asked us to put together some video clips that will help the In-Touch Agency understand what teenagers are like today—especially what their social interactions are like. The company's marketing manager has sent us a letter that describes the problems they're having and how we can help. I will read it now, and then we can talk about what kind of video clips we will make.

If you wish, give each participant a copy of the letter from the Marketing Manager of In-Touch Publishing, Inc. The "unexpected phone call" technique can work well in this drama. The president of the agency can send in an urgent message at any time to move things along.

Part 2: Recording and Reviewing the Interactions

Once the vice president of the advertising agency has set the scene, the agency executives choose and develop the scenes of typical behavior. Leaders help group members brainstorm ideas and rehearse the scenes to be recorded.

Specific instructions for continuing the process drama are given in Session 12.

Letter from In-Touch Publishing, Inc.

Dear Advertising Executives:

We are putting together a proposal for a new magazine, and we would like your agency to be a part of it. We're very excited about the prospect of reaching young people, but unfortunately, we feel that we are a bit out of touch with the current lifestyle of people your age (our company president just turned 90).

In order to write authentic stories for our readers, we need to know what young people's interactions look like. What kinds of things do they say to each other? What do they feel? How do they resolve conflicts? Sometimes, to us old folks, watching young people today communicate is like watching people speak in another language. We've heard that your staff understands this topic very well and might be willing to help us gain a better understanding of our readers.

Please let us know if you would be willing to take on this contract. Unfortunately, we have a rather tight deadline and need to have this job completed by _____.

Sincerely,

Ms. I. M. Outovitt

Marketing Manager

In-Touch Publishing, Inc.

References

Albert, L. (1996). *Cooperative discipline.* Circle Pines, MN: American Guidance Service.

Allen, J. (1977). The other side of the elephant: Theatre activities for classroom learning. Buffalo, NY: Crown Publishers.

American Psychiatric Association. (1996). Diagnostic and statistical manual of mental disorders (4th ed.). Washington, DC: Author.

American Psychiatric Association. (2000). *Diagnostic and statistical manual of mental disorders* (4th ed., text revision). Washington, DC: Author.

Attwood, T. (1998). *Asperger's syndrome: A guide for parents and professionals.* London: Jessica Kingsley.

Attwood, T. (2007). *The complete guide to Asperger's syndrome.* London: Jessica Kingsley.

Barkley, R. A. (1996). *Attention-deficit/hyperactivity disorder.* In E. Mash & R. A. Barkley (Eds.), *Child psychopathology* (pp. 63–112). New York: Guilford.

Barkley, R. A. (1998). *Attention-deficit/hyperactivity disorder: A handbook for diagnosis and treatment* (2nd ed.). New York: Guilford.

Barsky, M. & Mozenter, G. (1976). The use of creative drama in a children's group. *International Journal of Group Psychotherapy, 26,* 105–114.

Baron-Cohen, S., Jolliffe, T., Mortimore, C., & Robertson, M. (1997). Another advanced test of theory of mind: Evidence from very high functioning adults with autism or Asperger syndrome. *Journal of Child Psychology and Psychiatry, 38,* 813–822.

Baron-Cohen, S., Leslie, A. M., & Frith, U. (1985). Does the autistic child have a "theory of mind?" *Cognition, 21,* 37–46.

Baron-Cohen, S., Tager-Flusberg, H., & Cohen, D. J. (Eds.). (2000). *Understanding other minds: Perspectives from developmental cognitive neuroscience.* Oxford: Oxford University Press.

Baron-Cohen, S., & Wheelwright, S. (2004). The empathy quotient: An investigation of adults with Asperger syndrome or high functioning autism, and normal sex differences. *Journal of Autism and Developmental Disorders, 34,* 163–175.

Bashe, P., & Kirby, B. (2001). *The Oasis guide to Asperger syndrome.* New York: Crown Publishers.

Bowell, P., & Heap, B. S. (2001). *Planning process drama.* London: David Fulton Publishers.

Brown, D., Pryzwansky, W. B., & Schulte, A. C. (2001). *Psychological consultation and collaboration: Introduction to theory and practice.* New York: Allyn and Bacon.

Brumback, R. A., & Staton, R. (1982). An hypothesis regarding the commonality of right-hemisphere involvement in learning disability, attentional disorder, and childhood major depressive disorder. *Perceptual and Motor Skills, 55*, 1091–1097.

Bruner, J. S. (1998). Routes to reference. *Pragmatics and Cognition, 6*, 209–227.

Buege, C. (1993). The effect of mainstreaming on attitude and self-concept using creative drama and social skills training. *Youth Theatre Journal, 7*, 19–22.

Capps, L., Kehres, J., & Sigman, M. (1998). Conversational abilities among children with autism and children with developmental delays. *Autism, 2*, 325–344.

Carlson, S., & Moses, L. J. (2001). Individual differences in inhibitory control and children's theory of mind. *Child Development, 72*, 1032–1053.

Carroll, A., Bain, A., & Houghton, S. (1994). The effects of interactive video versus linear video on the levels of attention and comprehension of social behavior by children with attention disorders. *School Psychology Review, 23*, 29–43.

Cavell, T. A., Meehan, B. T., & Fiala, S. E. (2003). Assessing social competence in children and adolescents. In C. R. Reynolds & R. W. Kamphaus (Eds.), *Handbook of psychological and educational assessment of children: Personality, behavior, and context* (pp. 433–454). New York: Guilford.

Chang, E. C., & D'Zurilla, T. J. (1996). Relations between problem orientation and optimism, pessimism, and trait affectivity: A construct validation study. *Behaviour Research and Therapy, 34*, 185–194.

Ciarrochi, J., Scott, G., Deane, F. P., & Heaven, P. C. L. (2003). Relations between social and emotional competence and mental health: A construct validation study. *Personality and Individual Differences, 35*, 1947–1963.

Craig, J., & Baron-Cohen, S. (1999). Creativity and imagination in autism and Asperger syndrome. *Journal of Autism and Developmental Disorders, 29*, 319–325.

Cresci, M. M. (1989). *Creative dramatics for children*. New York: Scott, Foresman.

Crick, N. R., & Dodge, K. A. (1994). A review and reformulation of social information-processing mechanisms in children's social adjustment. *Psychological Bulletin, 115*, 74–101.

Damasio, A. R. (1994). *Descartes' error: Emotion, reason, and the human brain*. New York: Putnam.

de la Cruz, R. E., Lian, M. J., & Morreau, L. E. (1998). The effects of creative drama on social and oral language skills of children with learning disabilities. *Youth Theatre Journal, 12*, 89–95.

Denckla, M. B. (1979). Childhood learning disabilities. In K. M. Heilman & E. Valenstein (Eds.), *Clinical neuropsychology* (pp. 535–573). New York: Oxford University Press.

Deruelle, C., Rondan, C., Gepner, B., & Tardif, C. (2004). Spatial frequency and face processing in children with autism and Asperger syndrome. *Journal of Autism and Developmental Disorders, 34*, 199–210.

Dodge, K. A. (1986). A social information processing model of social competence in children. In M. Perlmutter (Ed.), *Minnesota Symposium on Child Psychology* (Vol. 18; pp. 77–125). Hillsdale, NJ: Erlbaum.

Dodge, K. A., & Crick, N. R. (1990). Social information processing bases of aggressive behavior in children. *Personality and Social Psychology Bulletin, 16,* 8–22.

Downs, A., & Smith, T. (2004). Emotional understanding, cooperation, and social behavior in high-functioning children with autism. *Journal of Autism and Developmental Disorders, 34,* 625–635.

Eagle, R. S. (2004). Commentary: Further commentary on the debate regarding increase in autism in California. *Journal of Autism and Developmental Disorders, 34,* 87–88.

Egan, G. J., Brown, R. T., Goonan, L., Goonan, B. T., & Celano, M. (1998). The development of decoding of emotions in children with externalizing behavioral disturbances and their normally developing peers. *Archives of Clinical Neuropsychology, 13,* 383–396.

Ehlers, S., & Gillberg, C. (1993). The epidemiology of Asperger syndrome: A total population study. *Journal of Child Psychology and Psychiatry, 34,* 1327–1350.

Fine, J. G., & Semrud-Clikeman, M. (2007, February). *Dynamic vs. static processing of faces in children with autistic spectrum disorders.* Paper presented at the annual meeting of the International Neuropsychological Society, Portland, OR.

Fletcher, J. M. (1989). Nonverbal learning disabilities and suicide: Classification leads to prevention. *Journal of Learning Disabilities, 22,* 176–179.

Forrest, B. J. (2004). The utility of math difficulties, internalized psychopathology, and visual-spatial deficits to identify children with a nonverbal learning disability syndrome: Evidence for a visual-spatial disability. *Child Neuropsychology, 10,* 129–146.

Frederick, B. P., & Olmi, D. J. (1994). Children with attention deficit hyperactivity disorder: A review of the literature on social skills deficits. *Psychology in the Schools, 31,* 288–296.

Frith, U., Happe, F., & Siddons, F. (1994). Autism and theory of mind in everyday life. *Social Development, 3,* 108–124.

Garfield, J. L., Peterson, C. C., & Perry, T. (2001). Social cognition, language acquisition, and the development of the theory of mind. *Mind and Language, 16,* 494–541.

Ghaziuddin, M., & Gerstein, L. (1996). Pedantic speaking style differentiates Asperger syndrome from high-functioning autism. *Journal of Autism and Developmental Disorders, 26,* 585–595.

Gilchrist, A., Green, J., Cox, A., Burton, D., Rutter, M, & Le Couteur, A. (2001). Development and current functioning in adolescents with Asperger syndrome: A comparative study. *Journal of Child Psychology and Psychiatry, 42,* 227–240.

Gouze, J. R. (1987). Attention and social problem-solving as correlates of aggression in preschool males. *Journal of Abnormal Child Psychology, 15,* 181–197.

Grady, S. (1995). *Overview: Project Soleil.* Unpublished manuscript, University of Texas at Austin.

Grady, S. (2000). *Drama and diversity: A pluralistic perspective for educational drama.* Portsmouth, NH: Heinemann.

Gresham, F. M. (1997). Social competence and students with behavior disorders: Where we've been, where we are, and where we should go. *Education and Treatment of Children, 20,* 233–249.

Gresham, F. M., & Elliott, S. (1990). *Social skills rating system.* Circle Pines, MN: American Guidance Service.

Gresham, F. M., Lane, K. L., MacMillan, D. L., Bocian, K. M., & Ward, S. L. (2000). Effects of positive and negative illusory biases: Comparisons across social and academic self-concept domains. *Journal of School Psychology, 38,* 151–175.

Gross-Tsur, V., Shalev, R. S., Manor, O., & Amir, N. (1995). Developmental right-hemisphere syndrome: Clinical spectrum of the nonverbal learning disability. *Journal of Learning Disabilities, 28,* 80–86.

Grossman J. B., Klin, A., Carter, A. S., & Volkmar, F. R.(2000). Verbal bias in recognition of facial emotion in children with Asperger syndrome. *Journal of Child Psychology and Psychiatry, 41,* 369–379.

Guli, L. A. (2004). *The effects of creative drama-based intervention for children with deficits in social perception.* Unpublished doctoral dissertation, University of Texas at Austin.

Gunter, H. L., Ghaziuddin, M., & Ellis, H. D. (2002). Asperger syndrome: Tests of right hemisphere functioning and interhemispheric communication. *Journal of Autism and Developmental Disorders, 32,* 263–281.

Hadwin, J., Baron-Cohen, S., Howlin, P., & Hill, K. (1997). Does teaching theory of mind have an effect on the ability to develop conversation in children with autism? *Journal of Autism and Developmental Disorders, 27,* 519–537.

Hala, S., Hug, S., & Henderson, A. (2003). Executive function and false-belief understanding in preschool children: Two tasks are harder than one. *Journal of Cognition and Development, 4,* 275–298.

Halberstadt, A. G., Denham, S. A., & Dunsmore, J. C. (2001). Affective social competence. *Social Development, 10,* 79–119.

Hall, C. W., Peterson, A. D., Webster, R. E., Bolen, L. M., & Brown, M. R. (1999). Perception of nonverbal social cues by regular education, ADHD, and ADHD/LD students. *Psychology in the Schools, 36,* 505–514.

Happe, F. (1994). An advanced test of theory of mind: Understanding of story characters' thought and feelings by able autistic, mentally handicapped and normal children and adults. *Journal of Autism and Developmental Disorders, 24(2),* 129–154.

Hartas, D. (1998). Non-verbal learning difficulties: More questions than answers. *Educational Psychology in Practice, 13,* 258–265.

Hayden, M. F. (1998). Civil rights litigation for institutionalized persons with mental retardation: A summary. *Mental Retardation, 36,* 75–83.

Heathcote, D. (1988). Drama as a process for change. In L. Johnson & C. O'Neill (Eds.), *Dorothy Heathcote: Collected writings on education and drama* (pp.114–125). London, England: Century Hutchinson Ltd.

Heathcote, D., & Bolton, G. (1995). *Drama for learning: Dorothy Heathcote's mantle of the expert approach to education.* Portsmouth, NH: Heinemann.

Heavey, L., Phillips, W., Baron-Cohen, S., & Rutter, M. (2000). The awkward moments test: A naturalistic measure of social understanding in autism. *Journal of Autism and Developmental Disorders, 30,* 225–236.

Howlin, P. (2003). Outcome in high-functioning adults with autism with and without early language delays: Implications for the differentiation between autism and Asperger syndrome. *Journal of Autism and Developmental Disorders, 33,* 3–13.

Huesmann, L. R., & Eron, L. D. (1989). Individual differences and the trait of aggression. *European Journal of Personality, 3,* 95–106.

Humphries, T., Cardy, J. O., Worling, D. E., & Peets, K. (2004). Narrative comprehension and retelling abilities of children with nonverbal learning disabilities. *Brain and Cognition, 56,* 77–88.

Hynd, G. W., Hern, K. L., Novey, E. S., Eliopulos, D., Marshall, R., Gonzalez, J. J., et al. (1993). Attention deficit-hyperactivity disorder and asymmetry of the caudate nucleus. *Journal of Child Neurology, 8,* 339–347.

Johnson, D. (1987). Nonverbal learning disabilities. *Pediatric Annals, 16*(2), 133–141.

Johnston, J. C., Healey, K. N., & Tracey, M. D. (1985). Drama and interpersonal problem solving: A dynamic interplay for adolescent groups. *Child Care Quarterly, 14,* 238–247.

Jolliffe, T., & Baron-Cohen, S. (1999). The strange stories test: A replication with high functioning adults with autism or Asperger syndrome. *Journal of Autism and Developmental Disorders, 29,* 395–406.

Joseph, R. M., & Tager-Flusberg, H. (2004). The relationship of theory of mind and executive functions to symptom type and severity in children with autism. *Development and Psychopathology, 16,* 137–155.

Kadesjo, B., Gillberg, C., & Hagberg, B. (1999). Autism and Asperger syndrome in seven-year-old-children: A total population study. *Journal of Autism and Developmental Disorders, 29,* 327–331.

Kanner, L. (1943). Autistic disturbances of affective contact. *Nervous Child, 2,* 217–250.

Klin, A., Volkmar, F. R., & Sparrow, S. S. (2000). Introduction. In A. Klin, F. R.Volkmar, & S. S. Sparrow (Eds.), *Asperger syndrome,* pp. 1–21. New York: Guilford.

Klin, A., Volkmar, F. R., Sparrow, S. S., Cicchetti, D. V., & Rourke, B. P. (1995). Validity and neuropsychological characterization of Asperger syndrome: Convergence with nonverbal learning disabilities syndrome. *Journal of Child Psychology and Psychiatry and Allied Disciplines, 36,* 1127–1140.

Laurent, A. C., & Rubin, E. (2004). Challenges in emotional regulation in Asperger syndrome and high-functioning autism. *Topics in Language Disorders, 24,* 286–297.

Lincoln, A., Courchesene, E., Allen, M., Hanson, E., & Ene, M. (1998). Neurobiology of Asperger syndrome: Seven case studies and quantitative magnetic resonance imaging findings. In E. Schopler, G. B. Mesibov, & L. J. Kunce (Eds.), *Asperger syndrome or high functioning autism? Current issues in autism* (pp. 145–163). New York: Plenum.

Little, L. (2002). Middle-class mothers' perceptions of peer and sibling victimization among children with Asperger's syndrome and nonverbal learning disorders. *Issues in Comprehensive Pediatric Nursing, 25,* 43–57.

Little, S. S. (1993). Nonverbal learning disabilities and socioemotional functioning: A review of recent literature. *Journal of Learning Disabilities, 26,* 653–665.

Lopez, B., & Leekam, S. R. (2003). Do children with autism fail to process information in context? *Journal of Child Psychology and Psychiatry, 44,* 285–300.

Martinez, J. (1989). *The role of empathic humor in counteracting burnout and promoting renewal.* Unpublished doctoral dissertation, University of Massachusetts, Amherst.

McCaslin, N. (1990). *Creative drama in the classroom.* Studio City, CA: Players Press.

McClure, B. A., Miller, G. A., & Russo, T. J. (1992). Conflict within a children's group: Suggestions for facilitating its expression and resolution strategies. *The School Counselor, 39,* 268–273.

McGovern, C. W., & Sigman, M. (2005). Continuity and change from early childhood to adolescence in autism. *Journal of Child Psychology and Psychiatry, 46,* 401–408.

Miller, J. N., & Ozonoff, S. (2000). The external validity of Asperger disorder: Lack of evidence from the domain of neuropsychology. *Journal of Abnormal Psychology, 109,* 227–238.

Neelands, J., & Goode, T. (2001). *Structuring drama work: A handbook of available forms in theatre and drama.* Cambridge, England: Cambridge University Press.

Neihart, M. (2000). Gifted children with Asperger's syndrome. *Gifted Child Quarterly, 44,* 222–225.

New Games Foundation. (1981). *More new games!* New York: Headlands Press.

Nikolaenko, N. N. (2004). Metaphorical and associative thinking in healthy children and in children with Asperger's syndrome at different ages. *Human Physiology, 30,* 532–536.

Nowicki, S., Jr., & Carton, E. (1997). The relation of nonverbal processing ability of faces and voices and children's feelings of depression and competence. *The Journal of Genetic Psychology, 158,* 357–363.

Nowicki, S., & Duke, M. P. (1994). Individual differences in the nonverbal communication of affect: The Diagnostic Analysis of Nonverbal Accuracy Scale. *Journal of Nonverbal Behavior, 18,* 9–35.

O'Neill, C. (1995). *Drama worlds: A framework for process drama.* Portsmouth, NH: Heinemann.

O'Neill, C., & Lambert, A. (1994). *Drama structures: A practical handbook for teachers.* Portsmouth, NH: Stanley Thornes Ltd.

Ozonoff, S., & Miller, J. N. (1995). Teaching theory of mind: A new approach to social skills training for individuals with autism. *Journal of Autism and Developmental Disorders, 25,* 415–433.

Pelletier, P. M., Ahmad, S. A., & Rourke, B. P. (2001). Classification rules for basic phonological processing disabilities and nonverbal learning disabilities: Formulation and external validity. *Child Neuropsychology, 7*(2), 84–98.

Pennington, B. F. (1991). *Diagnosing learning disorders: A neuropsychological framework.* New York: Guilford.

Peter, M. (2003). Drama, narrative and early learning. *British Journal of Special Education, 30,* 21–27.

Petti, V. L., Voelker, S. L., Shore, D. L., & Hayman-Abello, S. E. (2003). Perception of nonverbal emotion cues by children with nonverbal learning disabilities. *Journal of Developmental and Physical Disabilities 15*(1), 23–36.

Roeyers, H., Buysse, A., Ponnet, K., & Pichal, B. (2001). Advancing advanced mind-reading tests: Empathic accuracy in adults with a pervasive developmental disorder. *Journal of Child Psychology and Psychiatry, 42,* 271–278.

Rothenberg, S. (1998). *Nonverbal learning disabilities and social functioning.* Retrieved January 23, 2008, from www.nldontheweb.org/Rothenberg-1.htm

Rourke, B. P. (1989). *Nonverbal learning disabilities: The syndrome and the model.* New York: Guilford.

Rourke, B. P. (1995). *Syndrome of nonverbal learning disabilities: Neurodevelopmental manifestations.* New York: Guilford.

Rourke, B. P., Young, G. C., & Leenaars, A. A.(1989). A childhood learning disability that predisposes those afflicted to adolescent and adult depression and suicide risk. *Journal of Learning Disabilities, 22,* 169–175.

Rutherford, M. D., Baron-Cohen, S., & Wheelwright, S. (2002). Reading the mind in the voice: A study with normal adults and adults with Asperger syndrome and high functioning autism. *Journal of Autism and Developmental Disorders, 32,* 189–194.

Saarni, C. (1999). *The development of emotional competence.* New York: Guilford.

Safran, S. P. (2001). Asperger syndrome: The emerging challenge to special education. *Exceptional Children, 67,* 151–160.

Saltz, E. M., & Brodie, J. (1982). Pretend-play training in childhood: A review and critique. In D. J. Pepler & K. H. Rubin (Eds.), *The play of children: Current theory and research* (pp. 97–113). New York: Karger.

Schatz, A. M., Weimer, A. K, & Trauner, D. A. (2002). Brief report: Attention differences in Asperger syndrome. *Journal of Autism and Developmental Disorders, 32,* 333–336.

Schultz, R. T., Romanski, L. M., & Tsatsanis, K. D. (2000). Neurofunctional models of autistic disorder and Asperger syndrome. In A. Klin, F. R. Volkmar, & S. S. Sparrow (Eds.), *Asperger syndrome.* New York: Guilford.

Semrud-Clikeman, M. (2007). *Social competence.* New York: Springer Science and Business Media.

Semrud-Clikeman, M., & Hynd, G. W. (1990). Right hemispheric dysfunction in nonverbal learning disabilities: Social, academic, and adaptive functioning in adults and children. *Psychological Bulletin, 107,* 196–209.

Semrud-Clikeman, M., & Schafer, V. (2000). Social competence and developmental disorders. *Journal of Psychotherapy in Independent Practice, 1*(4), 3–19.

Sherratt, D., & Peter, M. (2002). *Developing play and drama in children with autistic spectrum disorders.* London, England: David Fulton Publishers.

Shewchuk, R. M., Johnson, M. O., & Elliott, T. R. (2000). Self-appraised social problem solving abilities, emotional reactions, and actual problem solving performance. *Behaviour Research and Therapy, 38,* 727–740.

Shriberg, L. D., Paul, R., McSweeny, J. L., Klin, A., Cohen, D. J., & Volkmar, F. R. (2001). Speech and prosody characteristics of adolescents and adults with high functioning autism and Asperger syndrome. *Journal of Speech, Language and Hearing Research, 44,* 1097–1115.

Singh, S. D., Ellis, C. R., Winton, A. S., Singh, N. N., Leung, J. P., & Oswald, D. P. (1998). Recognition of facial expressions of emotion by children with attention-deficit hyperactivity disorder. *Behavior Modification, 22,* 128–142.

Sparrow, S. (1997). Developmentally based assessments. In D. J. Cohen & F. R. Volkmar (Eds.), *Handbook of autism and pervasive developmental disorders.* New York: Wiley.

Spitzberg, B. H. (2003). Methods of interpersonal skill assessment. In J. O. Greene & B. R. Burleson (Eds.), *Handbook of communication and social interaction skills* (pp. 93–134). Mahwah, NJ: Erlbaum.

Spolin, V. (1986). *Theater games for the classroom.* Evanston, IL: Northwestern University Press.

Stewig, J. W. (1972). Creative drama and language growth. *Elementary School Journal, 72,* 176–188.

Stirtzinger, R., & Robson, B. (1985). Videodrama and the observing ego. *Small Group Behavior, 16,* 539–548.

Stone, V. E., Baron-Cohen, S., & Knight, R. T. (1998). Frontal lobe contributions to theory of mind. *Journal of Cognitive Neuroscience, 10,* 640–656.

Tager-Flusberg, H. (1999). A psychological approach to understanding the social and language impairments in autism. *International Review of Psychiatry, 11,* 325–334.

Tanguay, P. E. (2000). Pervasive developmental disorders: A 10-year review. *Journal of the American Academy of Child and Adolescent Psychiatry, 39,* 1079–1095.

Tantum, D. (2000). Psychological disorder in adolescents and adults with Asperger syndrome. *Autism, 4,* 47–62.

Tarlington, C., & Verriour, P. (1991). *Role drama.* Portsmouth, NH: Heinemann.

Teeter, P. A., & Semrud-Clikeman, M. (1997). *Child neuropsychology: Assessment and interventions for neurodevelopmental disorders.* Needham Heights, MA: Allyn and Bacon.

Thompson, S. (1997). *The source for nonverbal learning disorders.* East Moline, IL: LinguiSystems, Inc.

Toichi, M., & Kamio, Y. (2003). Long-term memory in high-functioning autism: Controversy on episodic memory in autism reconsidered. *Journal of Autism and Developmental Disorders, 33,* 151–161.

Tsai, L. Y. (1999). Medical treatment in autism. In D. B. Zanger (Ed.), *Autism: Identification, education, and treatment* (pp. 199–257). Mahwah, NJ: Erlbaum.

Voeller, K. K. S. (1986). Right-hemisphere deficit syndrome in children. *American Journal of Psychiatry, 143,* 1004–1009.

Voeller, K. K. S. (1994). Techniques for measuring social competence in children. In G. R. Lyon (Ed.), *Frames of reference for the assessment of learning disabilities: New views on measurement issues* (pp. 523–554). Baltimore: Paul H. Brookes.

Voeller, K. K. S. (1995). Clinical neurologic aspects of the right-hemisphere deficit syndrome. *Journal of Child Neurology, 10*(1), S16–S22.

Volkmar, F. R., & Klin, A. (2000). Diagnostic issues in Asperger syndrome. In A. Klin, F. R. Volkmar, & S. S. Sparrow (Eds.), *Asperger syndrome*. New York: Guilford.

Volkmar, F. R., Klin, A., Schultz, R.T., Rubin, E., & Bronin, R. (2000). Asperger's disorder. *American Journal of Psychiatry, 157*, 262–267.

Vygotsky, L. S. (1978). *Mind in society: The development of higher psychological processes.* Cambridge, MA: MIT Press.

Walsh, R. T. (1990). A creative arts program in social skills training for early adolescents: An exploratory study. *The Arts in Psychotherapy, 17*, 131–137.

Walsh, R. T., Kosidoy, M., & Swanson, L. (1991). Promoting social-emotional development through creative drama for students with special needs. *Canadian Journal of Community Mental Health, 10*, 153–166.

Walsh-Bowers, R. T. (1992). A creative drama prevention program for easing early adolescents' adjustment to school transitions. *The Journal of Primary Prevention, 13*, 131–147.

Warger, C. L. (1984). Creative drama for autistic adolescents: Expanding leisure and recreation options. *Journal of Child and Adolescent Psychotherapy, 1*, 15–19.

Warner, D. J. (1996). Mirroring movement for increasing family cooperation. *Journal of Family Psychotherapy, 7*, 85–88.

Waters, E., & Sroufe, L. A. (1983). Social competence as a developmental construct. *Developmental Review, 3*, 79–97.

What is autism: An overview. (n.d.). Retrieved April 17, 2008, from the Autism Speaks Web site: www.autisimspeaks.org/whatisit/index.php

Wing, L. (1981). Asperger's syndrome: A clinical account. *Journal of Autism and Developmental Disorders, 29*, 327–331.

Wing, L. (1991). The relationship between Asperger's syndrome and Kanner's autism. In U. Frith (Ed.), *Autism and Asperger syndrome* (pp. 93–121). Cambridge, England: Cambridge University Press.

Woods, S. P., Weinborn, M., Ball, J. D, Tiller-Nevin, S., & Pickett, T. C. (2000). Periventricular leukomalacia (PVL): An identical twin case study illustration of white matter dysfunction and nonverbal learning disability (NLD). *Child Neuropsychology, 6*(4), 274–285.

Worling, D. E., Humphries, T., & Tannock, R. (1999). Spatial and emotional aspects of language inferencing in nonverbal learning disabilities. *Brain and Language, 70*, 220–239.

About the Authors

LAURA A. GULI received her Ph.D. from the University of Texas at Austin in 2004, where she conducted dissertation research investigating the Social Competence Intervention Program. She received a full University Continuing Fellowship Award in 2002 for academic excellence and contributions. She completed her internship and postdoctoral work at Salesmanship Club Youth and Family Centers in Dallas and the Austin Independent School District, respectively. Dr. Guli has authored several academic articles and chapters in addition to presenting her work at several national conferences. Prior to her career in psychology, she was a teacher of elementary drama and art. Currently, Dr. Guli is working in private practice as a licensed psychologist in the state of Texas. She continues to be interested in working with and learning more about children with autistic spectrum disorders and related disabilities.

ALISON D. WILKINSON received her Ph.D. in school psychology at the University of Texas at Austin in 2006. She completed her postdoctoral fellowship in pediatric neuropsychology at the University of Minnesota Medical Center in 2008. Currently, she is a pediatric neuropsychologist at Children's Medical Center in Dallas. Dr. Wilkinson has presented research related to social competence at several national and international conferences and has specialized training in the assessment of autism spectrum disorders. She is continually inspired by the wit and perseverance of children with social competence disorders and their families.

MARGARET SEMRUD-CLIKEMAN, Ph.D., received her doctorate from the University of Georgia in 1990. She completed an internship and postdoctoral fellowship at the Massachusetts General Hospital/Harvard Medical School (MGH) and received a postdoctoral neuroscience fellowship at MGH from the National Institutes of Mental Health to study neuropsychological and brain morphology in children with AD/HD. Her dissertation received the Outstanding Dissertation of the Year Award from the Orton Dyslexia Society. In 1999, Dr. Semrud-Clikeman was awarded the Early Career Contributions Award from the National Academy of Neuropsychology. She has published more than 30 articles, 40 chapters, and four books. Dr. Semrud-Clikeman and her students developed and piloted the Social Competence Intervention Program while at the University of Texas at Austin. Currently a professor at Michigan State University with a joint appointment in psychology and psychiatry, she is engaged in conducting research on AD/HD, 18q-syndrome, and autism spectrum disorders.